ONE HUNDRED MILES FROM HOME

 CINCINNATI, OHIO

ONE HUNDRED MILES FROM HOME

Nuclear Contamination in
the Communities of the
Ohio River Valley:
Mound, Paducah, Piketon,
Fernald, Maxey Flats and
Jefferson Proving Ground

Carol Rainey

Foreword by Wendell Berry

Little Miami Press

ISBN-13: 978-0-9796327-2-3

Cover photograph of the Ohio River by Mona Weiner.
Cover design by Kathryn Kennedy.

Publisher's Cataloguing-in-Publication

Rainey, Carol, 1942-
    One hundred miles from home : nuclear contamination in the communi-
ties of the Ohio River Valley : Mound, Paducah, Piketon, Fernald, Maxey
Flats, and Jefferson Proving Ground / Carol Rainey ; foreword by Wendell
Berry. -- 1st ed.
    p. cm.
    Includes bibliographical references and index.
    ISBN-13: 978-0-9796327-2-3
    ISBN-10: 0-9796327-2-2

    1. Radioactive pollution--Ohio. 2. Radioactive pollution--Kentucky. 3.
Radioactive pollution--Indiana. 4. Nuclear weapons plants--Environmental
aspects--Ohio. 5. Nuclear weapons plants--Environmental aspects--Kentucky.
6. Jefferson Proving Ground (Ind.)-- Environmental conditions. I. Title. II.
Title: 100 miles from home.

TD196.R3R35 2008   363.17'9909771
                         QBI08-600136

To order contact Little Miami Press

LittleMiamiPress@fuse.net

in memory of Denise and Marion

and

for all who spoke up

The problem in defense is how far you can go without destroying from within what you are trying to defend from without.

Eisenhower

There appears to be a need for adequate education of the people of our country concerning the radiological hazards resulting from atomic explosions. This should be realistic in nature with the view to giving the public the correct understanding of this matter in order that the hysterical and alarmist complex now so prevalent may be corrected....Alleviation of their fears would be a matter of reeducation over a long period of time...until the public will accept the possibility of an atomic explosion within a hundred or so miles of their homes....

From a memorandum prepared for the Army Chief of Staff in 1946 during plans to find a nuclear test site in the United States

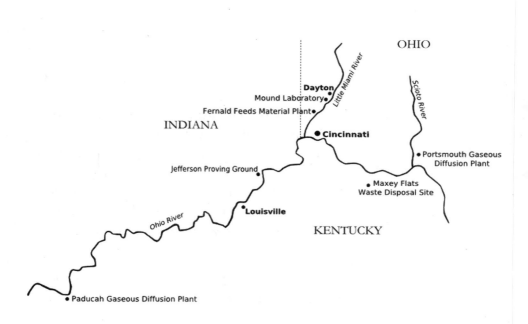

OHIO

Little Miami River

Scioto River

Dayton
Mound Laboratory●
Fernald Feeds Material Plant●

INDIANA

● **Cincinnati**

● Portsmouth Gaseous
   Diffusion Plant

Jefferson Proving Ground●

● Maxey Flats
   Waste Disposal Site

Ohio River

●**Louisville**

KENTUCKY

● Paducah Gaseous Diffusion Plant

TABLE OF CONTENTS

1. *Foreword* **by Wendell Berry** i

2. *Introduction: Atom Valley* *1*

Since the 1950s Cincinnati has been the "hub" of nuclear developments in the Ohio River Valley. At the beginning of the Cold War, state and local political leaders were eager to acquire government contracts, having little awareness of the dangers of radioactive materials. In the 1950s the *New York Times* referred to the region as "Atom Valley." At the present time six locations which were involved in nuclear weapons production in the early years are responding to the radioactive and chemical contamination of the land and water. Two of the sites are being considered as possible locations for new nuclear installations, which would bring the threat of future contamination. This book tells the stories of the six sites.

3. *Hill of Secrets: Mound Laboratory,*
Miamisburg, Ohio 7

Mound was an early research laboratory outside of Dayton which produced polonium for the first atomic bombs, and later became a center for various kinds of nuclear research involving tritium, uranium, plutonium and thorium. It created the plutonium batteries which for fifty years were used to power spacecraft. Mound closed in 1993 and a "fast-track" cleanup made parts of the original site available for commercial development. Former workers and residents, many with health problems, are continuing to have difficulty acquiring plant records to verify how much radiation they were exposed to.Much of the work Mound did in the early years is still classified.

4. *The Hidden Plutonium: Paducah Uranium Enrichment Plant,*
Paducah, Kentucky 37

The plant at Paducah used a gaseous diffusion method to produce low-level enriched uranium for nuclear power plants and nuclear warheads. Careless operation of the plant resulted in radioactive and chemical contamination of the ecosystem. The generation of electricity to operate the gaseous diffusion cascades also resulted in the release of large amounts of carbon dioxide emissions. In 1999 it was revealed that workers at Paducah had not been told that some of the uranium they were working with was "reprocessed" and contaminated with plutonium and other transuranic elements, nor had they been protected against exposure. At the present time Paducah is the only uranium enrichment plant still operating in the United States. Though it is due to close some time within the next five years, local officials have received funds to explore the possibility of building a new nuclear plant on site, which would bring the danger of new contamination.

5. *Future of Uncertainty: Portsmouth Uranium Enrichment Plant, Piketon, Ohio* *63*

The gaseous diffusion plant at Piketon, Ohio on the Scioto River north of Portsmouth received the low-enriched (3-5%) uranium from Paducah, and until 1991 enriched it further (up to 97%) to make it usable in nuclear weapons and nuclear submarines. Like Paducah, the plant at Piketon left radioactive-- and particularly extensive chemical contamination-- of the land and water, and workers with multiple health problems. Though the old gaseous diffusion operation is now closed, the privately-owned United States Enrichment Corporation (USEC) hopes to open a huge new enrichment plant at Piketon using a centrifuge model. Its plans, however, are encountering many technical and financial difficulties. It's also possible, that Piketon, like Paducah, could be chosen to be the site of a new reprocessing plant or a waste disposal site, under the GNEP of the Bush Administration. Rumors that Piketon will become a 'temporary' storage dump for high level waste, because of continuing problems with Yucca Mountain, are alarming local residents a great deal.

6. *The Uranium Leak: Feed Materials Production Plant, Fernald, Ohio* *95*

The Fernald plant north of Cincinnati produced uranium ingots for the reactors at Hanford and Savannah River which created plutonium for warheads. It made national headlines in 1984 when it was revealed that for forty years tons of uranium emissions had been released into the atmosphere, inhaled by workers and nearby residents The land and the underlying aquifer were also contaminated. Fernald is now closed and part of its land has been converted to a nature preserve, but 80% of its waste remains in containment facilities on site, which will have to be monitored for billions of years.

7. *Tritium in the Maple Trees: Maxey Flats Low-Level Disposal Site,*
    Maxey Flats, Kentucky *127*

Maxey Flats was a private nuclear waste storage facility located in eastern Kentucky. When it opened in the 1960s it was initially to be a depository for low-level waste from commercial, medical, and research facilities, but government and/or management decisions allowed it to become a storage facility for high-level waste from nuclear power and nuclear weapons production sites. It was closed in 1977 when it was revealed that high levels of contamination, including plutonium and tritium, were already in the water and the ecosystem. The waste could not be removed from the site, and is presently contained and heavily monitored. The hill of waste there, like the waste at Fernald, will essentially have to be monitored forever.

8. *The Littered Battleground: Jefferson Proving Ground,*
    Southeastern Indiana *147*

Jefferson Proving Ground near Madison, Indiana opened in 1941 to test army munitions, but became part of the nuclear history of the region in the 1980s when it began to test projectiles made from depleted uranium. It closed in 1989 and part of the site was turned into a national wildlife refuge. Because of unexploded ordinances in the other part of the site, however, the Army says that it cannot remove the depleted uranium and, despite local objections, wishes to leave and end environmental testing and monitoring.

9. *Conclusion: The New Danger* *167*

Though the six sites in the Ohio River Valley are all in various stages of remediation, there are still questions as to how successful the cleanups have been and how well the sites will be monitored in the future. There are also questions as the role the sites may play if Bush Administration plans for a nuclear revival continue. The closing of the EPA libraries to public access may make future independent investigations into the effects of the contamination difficult. An atmosphere of secrecy now surrounds the government's nuclear plans just as it did in the 1950s when the these plants were first built.

10. *Appendices* *173*
    The Nuclear Fuel Cycle
    Glossary of Terms

11. *Sources* *185*

12. *Index* *189*

FOREWORD
BY
WENDELL BERRY

The six stories told in this book affect us all. They concern us urgently. As presented here, they are exhaustively documented, understood with exemplary intelligence, and brilliantly told. Carol Rainey here makes of story telling a work of patriotism. Her work is as compellingly readable as it is horrifying. It can become less horrifying only by being widely read and taken to heart.

Each of these six stories is about a place used for the purpose of nuclear war or "peaceful": nuclear power. They actually are six versions of the same story: how a place, once merely a part of our only inhabitable planet, became a place of contamination, of ecological and human disease. Some of them will need to be monitored for billions of years. The need for an already failed human respon-sibility to be effective for billions of years is of course the blackest of black jokes. Each of these stories is about the evolution of techno-scientific sophisti-cation and bravado into a black joke.

And so this is, in a sense almost biblical, a book of revelation. Most pro-foundly and disturbingly, it reveals the disparity between the reputation of modern science, a romantic quest for exact knowledge and ultimate truth, and the actual performance of that science as applied to earthly and practical aims. In each of the six places of this accounting the application of exact knowledge and precise methodology has produced a mess, and not only a mess but a grave danger that is, within the limits of human comprehension, permanent.

In the beginning, typically, these installations were seen as unmitigated goods, eagerly approved and paid for by the federal government. Four of them were eagerly solicited and competed for by local governments. And every one of those official authorizations was the sort of unfounded and misplaced act of faith which, in our right minds, we recognize as superstition.

As if it has not been shown sufficiently elsewhere, this book shows us again the ruthlessness of our economic system. Within the framework of industrial morality, and under pressure of profit-making or technological progress or official secrecy, people and their places are held perfectly in contempt. Consider also the neighbors of the U.S. Department of Energy Hanford site in Washington state. Consider also the "down winders" of Utah.

And these stories force upon us again and again the realization that nuclear weapons have fundamentally changed the definition of war. Once we could believe without too much trouble that war was contest of two opposing sides, in which an advantage to one side was a disadvantage to the other. Now we know that each side's nuclear armament inflicts in inevitable damage on both sides, a damage at once moral and physical. With these weapons a variety of "friendly fire" is a necessary result.

The history of nuclear technology is now more than half a century old. In condemning it, we are hardly rushing to judgment. Now surely we must ask the question that, on the evidence of this book and much other evidence, we cannot honesty avoid: When great, undisputable quantities of lethal waste are acculumulated, at ecological and human and economic costs that are unimaginable, must we not account the whole enterprise a waste and a tragic mistake? From a point of view entirely practical, it is clear that we have not developed, and that we undoubtedly cannot develop, a political-scientific-industrial organization competent to deal with the effects of long-lasting poisons and pollutants.

Ultimately we are going to have to respond sensibly to the fact that we humans are not intelligent enough, are too morally lazy, too careless, too willing to shift responsibility, to work safely on large scale at the risk of great and permanent damage. We are, in fact, creatures more humble and more superficial than we like to think. As the great Canadian ecologist Stan Rowe wrote twenty years ago, "we are Earthlings, out of Mother Earth and her moon rhythms, our bodies composed of the surface substances that lie ready at hand: star dust, humus, air and water. Notably we are not composed of heavy metals, radionuclides, petroleum hydrocarbons, nor any of those unnatural resources that we persist in digging out from underground to poison and pollute the planet and ourselves."

Port Royal, Kentucky
February 20, 2008

INTRODUCTION:

ATOM VALLEY

When I was a child in the 1950s I remember seeing the hydrogen bomb clouds on the front page of the *Cincinnati Post* and overhearing my mother and grandmother talk about whether or not the end of the world was coming. Such images were the reason I carried nuclear awareness into adulthood and became opposed to the idea of war. Then I put the nuclear issue out of my head, studying literature and becoming a teacher. It was the experience of reading *The Fate of the Earth* in 1982 which put nuclear weapons back into my thinking again: the dangers had not gone away, but in thirty years time had only intensified. Weapons had become so destructive that their intentional--or accidental-- release could lead to annihilation. Scientists were talking about a nuclear winter, a planet completely uninhabitable. During the next few years I worked for the local chapter of the nuclear freeze, and protested at the Nevada Test Site. Gorbachev's initiatives to end the Cold War, leading to the U.S. and Soviet decisions to begin dismantling the nuclear arsenals, brought a sense of relief. The Bush election of 2000, however, with the sudden new burst in military spending, including nuclear spending, and talk about preemptive first strikes, made me realize the giant was not dead, but only hiding. The Bush government, against all reason, was threatening to use nuclear weapons again, increasing instability, danger, and fear throughout the world.

In 2001 I organized a local nuclear study group to learn more about the current nuclear danger and figure out what we could do. We held a workshop on depleted uranium and learned how it had been used in the Gulf War. One member of the group suggested we visit the site of the old uranium enrichment plant in Piketon, Ohio to learn more about local nuclear production facilities. When we first went to Piketon, I barely knew what enriched uranium was. We learned the old operation was closed, but a new enrichment plant was being built. Piketon activists told us about worker illnesses and contaminated soil and water. I had heard about the contamination at Hanford and Rocky Flats. I also knew there had been contamination at the Fernald plant north of Cincinnati, but the newspapers said the site was being cleaned up. It never occurred to me to wonder if the local locations might still be dangerous.

After the Piketon trip I began to investigate the history of the local plants. Cincinnati, I discovered, had been *surrounded* by nuclear installations, all of which had left contamination. Someone in our group said, why don't you do a fact sheet about these places, which we can distribute here locally? At first that was my intent. The more I read, however, the deeper, more complex, and far-reaching I found the information to be, and I realized the sites were part of a much larger story.

In the 1950s Cincinnati had been considered the "hub" of new atomic developments. The newspapers of the time expressed pride that our nuclear sites were so important in Cold War foreign policy, even that the city was growing in national importance because of them. (1) A local story said, "The Ohio [River] rolls by what is probably the greatest concentration of atomic installations in the world." (2) A few years later a *New York Times* writer said the region should be called "Atom Valley." (3) Cincinnati leaders in the fifties eagerly sought these installations. In fact, in 1952 while the Fernald plant was being built, some leaders also tried to get the huge uranium enrichment plant--which eventually went to Piketon--located in Butler County near Fernald. (4) Local industry supported and prospered from the nuclear buildup. Procter and Gamble, a symbol of corporate Cincinnati and household cleanliness, quietly operated a nuclear weapons assembly plant (from 1951 to 1959) in Amarillo, Texas. From 1957-1959 the former president of P&G, Neil McElroy, served as Eisenhower's Secretary of Defense during the height of the nuclear buildup. (5) General Electric Aircraft Engines researched the possible use of nuclear energy to power airplanes (an idea which the *Cincinnati Enquirer* at the time said had "unimagined possibilities," but fortunately for the world didn't work out). (6)

The six nuclear installations in the Cincinnati area differed in their size and function: there was a research lab, two enrichment plants, a uranium foundry, a radioactive waste disposal site, and an army firing range. After several years of research I decided to write a historical survey of each of these local sites, describing what went on at the plants, the response of workers and residents when they became aware of the dangers, and the level of the contamination today.

It was not easy to get information. I relied heavily on local newspapers to get basic data, but had to keep in mind biases and omissions. For years the government operated the plants in an atmosphere of secrecy, so not a lot of information was made available to anyone. The Atomic Energy Commission, and later the Department of Energy, also often gave misleading, if not dishonest, information about the dangers of the work, particularly in the early years. Even the scientific studies they commissioned, when cancers began to appear, were sometimes politically biased. Records about how much radiation workers and residents were exposed to had not been kept, or were kept haphazardly, or sometimes even fabricated. Scientists had to do "dose reconstruction" of exposures, and base their conclusions about the connection of radiation to illness on these kinds of numbers. Those scientists who came up with results the government didn't like sometimes lost their funding. Because I am not a scientist, I have had to rely primarily on what historical sources I could find, a limitation of this study I admit, but one I couldn't avoid. Though the Department of Energy prides itself on having public impact hearings today about its nuclear proposals, the reports discussed at the hearings are so technical it is often difficult for lay people to understand them. For the most part Americans are still kept isolated from, and ignorant about, the dangers of the nuclear world.

In a way I have written this book still to be a kind of fact sheet, for the people of the Ohio River Valley first of all--and for those communities in Texas, Nevada, Utah, New Mexico and Idaho which now have much of our waste--but also for other workers, residents, and activists throughout the country, and throughout the world, who are trying to get information about the nuclear presence in their own communities. I have also written this book for those who support the revival of nuclear power and nuclear weapons, to make real to them what it is like to live in a radioactively contaminated world which may be a threat to life forever.

The most recent publication of the National Academy of Science on the Biological Effects of Ionizing Radiation (BEIR VII), published in the summer of 2005, supports the theory that there is *no* safe dose level for ionizing radiation exposure. (7) This "linear no threshold theory" means that all ionizing radiation is dangerous to living cells, either immediately or long-term. If this theory turns out to be true, the health implications are staggering. A second important point is that there are now millions of tons of radioactive waste in this country and throughout the world. At the present time no technology exists which can render these radioactive materials completely harmless. Containment strategies exist and new ones are being developed, but we have no guarantee that these strategies will work for the millions, in some cases, billions of years the waste will remain radioactive. This basic knowledge about our nuclear world must be kept in our consciousness, as we evolve new political strategies and styles of leadership to deal with the responsibilities which face us.

Notes: Introduction

1. "Cincinnati Hub of Atom Plant Installations," *Cincinnati Enquirer,* August 14, 1952, 12.

2. "Ohio River Flows into Atomic Age," *Cincinnati Enquirer,* October 18, 1954, 39.

3. Rutter, Richard, "The Ohio Becomes Industrial Aorta," *New York Times,* November 20, 1955, F1.

4. "AEC Plans $800 Million Atom Plant," *Cincinnati Enquirer,* April 3, 1952, 1.

5. *Procter & Gamble: The House that Ivory Built.* (Lincolnville, Ill.: NTC Business Books, 1988), 21-22, 26.

6. "Cincinnati Hub" 12.

7. Vedentam, Shankar, "Low Radiation Doses Still Pose Risks, Panel Finds," *Washington Post,* June 30, 2005, A7.

Hill of Secrets:

The Mound Laboratory,

Miamisburg, Ohio

Forty miles north of Cincinnati in the area of Miamisburg, Ohio is a large conical earthwork known as the Miamisburg Mound, believed to have been built by the Adena Indians who lived in the Great Miami River valley over 2,000 years ago. Some archeologists believe its 80-foot height indicates it may have been used as a signal mound, a way of communicating with other tribes throughout the southern Ohio region. Its secret tunnels and vaults may also have been used for burials.

Up to the 1700s this area in southern Ohio was inhabited by Shawnee and Miami Indians who had trails along the Great Miami and Little Miami Rivers. In the 1790s settlers came north on the Great Miami and eventually settled in the area of what today is Dayton. In the 1820s parts of the Miami and Erie Canal were built which eventually linked the Ohio River to Lake Erie in the north; the canal flourished for twenty years, eventually being replaced by railroads. The city of Dayton developed industries and by the early 20th century was a center of innovative technology. Thomas and Hochwalt Laboratory invented the fire extinguisher. Charles Kettering invented the automatic ignition for cars. Dayton, of course, was also the home of the Wright brothers. In 1911 they built their first airplane factory, and today the city is generally known as the birth-place of aviation.

Thomas and Hochwalt Laboratory was eventually taken over by Monsanto Chemical. In 1943 Charles A. Thomas, the research director of Monsanto, was contacted by James B. Conant, who was then involved in secret research on the Manhattan Project. Conant asked Thomas to investigate the chemistry of Polonium-210, which the scientists wanted to mix with the element beryllium so that neutrons could be released to initiate, or "trigger," the chain reaction in the atomic bomb. (1) Polonium is an extremely radioactive, highly toxic element which is capable of generating an enormous amount of heat. It is rare in nature and no pure metallic form had existed before the Dayton Monsanto lab was given its assignment. Thomas and his associates extracted and purified polonium from bismuth using a complex chemical process. He was sworn to secrecy, and many of the first researchers were not even told what the polonium would be used for. Their research was known simply as the Dayton Project.

Early research was conducted in a number of small facilities in Dayton, including the Bonebrake Theological Seminary building on West First Street. Later the research moved to the Runnymede Playhouse in Oakwood, a massive glass-topped structure which had originally been built as a recreational facility for Thomas' in-laws. "Between big trucks rolling in and out," one neighbor said, "the floodlights and power lines strung all over, the place was a real mess." (2) A former worker said employees in the laboratories used only rubber gloves and ventilators to protect them from radiation, so contamination was always a risk, not only for them but unwary residents nearby. When workers became "too hot" with radiation, they stopped what they were doing and only returned to the labs when their bodies had cooled down. (3) In 1950 the playhouse was demolished, its debris taken away and buried, for reasons no one at the time understood. Fifty years later the Ohio EPA, investigating the sites of this early nuclear research, said that elevated concentrations of Polonium-210 were still evident near the Bonebrake Seminary. The site was recommended to the Army Corps of Engineers' FUSRAP (Formerly Utilized Site Remedial Action Program) which was responsible for "cleaning up" many small locations which had conducted nuclear research in the early years of the atomic age. Though the Ohio Department of Health said in 2004 that the polonium offered no *immediate health risk* [italics added], it suggested further study. (4) Polonium-210 has a very short half-life (210 days) so would not still have been highly radioactive, but it is, like other radioactive elements, extremely toxic and may have left contaminants in the soil. (Polonium-210 was the substance allegedly used to poison former Russian spy Alexander Litvinenko in the fall of 2006. Reports at the time said that Polonium-210 is a trillion times more toxic than cyanide.) (5)

After World War II Congress established the Atomic Energy Commission, a five member committee to develop and control the U.S. atomic energy program. Though a civilian agency, its members were appointed by the president and in the early years gave unquestioning support for Truman's plans to expand nuclear weapons production and make the United States a nuclear powerhouse. Truman felt a large nuclear arsenal necessary to intimidate other world powers, especially the Soviet Union, and assure American dominance of the post-war world. (6) Some of the Manhattan Project scientists regarded the power within the atom as dangerous, because still not well understood, and had advised Truman to share information with scientists in other countries to prevent a bomb-building competition, fearing that a nuclear arms race could spin out of control. Their advice, however, was ignored. In the late 1940s scientists on the General Advisory Council of the Atomic Energy Commission recommended that America not develop the hydrogen bomb because they saw it as an instrument of genocide. (7) Truman chose to ignore them as well. At the time, scientists had little knowledge about the long-term biological effects of radiation, and politicians such as Truman had no knowledge at all. In 1945, two days after the bombing of Hiroshima, Dr. Harold Jacobson, one of the Manhattan Project scientists, had predicted with eerie accuracy that the effects of radiation from the bombing might be far worse than the immediate dangers from the blast and fire, but he had been ridiculed by Oppenheimer, demoted, and investigated by the FBI. (8) From the beginning, that is, the federal government presented the atomic bomb as a symbol of America's "strength," and any criticism of nuclear weapons was viewed as unpatriotic, no matter how scientifically or medically justified the criticism was.

ii

In 1946 as plans for nuclear weapons production proceeded, the Atomic Energy Commission decided, in gratitude to Charles Thomas, to build a permanent polonium production plant in Miamisburg, ten miles south of Dayton, which would be the first permanent facility of the AEC. Miamisburg had once been a small rural community of flour mills, timber mills and tobacco fields. The most significant event in its early history had been the massive flooding of the Great Miami River in March, 1913, which caused water to cover most of the greater Dayton area. Bridges and remnants of the old canal had been demolished; much of the town and surrounding farms had been devastated. Immediately afterwards levies and dams had been built to prevent future floodings. (9)

The Monsanto Mound Laboratory--named for the earthwork nearby--was built on a high 306-acre hill, 1,000 feet east of the Great Miami River, overlying the Great Miami Aquifer, which extends as far north as Dayton and as far south as Cincinnati, and is a major water supplier for the region. As with the other nuclear sites to be discussed, the location of the plant near a large water source was essential, since water was necessary for the plant's cooling operations and--most significantly later--the disposal of waste. The construction of the plant took almost two years and cost $25.5 million dollars. Part of Mound was built into a hill with a drainage ditch below. According to a Dayton news story, so much concrete was used in the construction--in some places walls were 16 feet thick--that commercial concrete contracts for other projects were shut down in three states until the plant was finished. (10)

Mound Laboratory opened in 1948 with 450 employees. At the opening ceremony, a spokesperson for the AEC described the new facility as "a research laboratory for the investigation of the basic chemical problems in the field of atomic energy." (11) What actually went on at the plant, however, was largely kept secret from the public, and many of the details of Mound's history are still classified. In the 1950s it was a tight, cerebral, intense research laboratory. The widow of James M. Goode, a physicist who had worked at Mound in the 1950s, said, "There was pressure on [the scientists] because nobody knew what was happening on the other side of the world....They were a bunch of cowboys. They wanted to find out [things] first before the Soviets." (Goode died in 1960 at the age of 36 of Hodgkin's disease, a death his daughter today is investigating.) (12)

Mound had its own water and sanitary sewage lines, and the town of Miamisburg regarded it in a way as "its own city." (13) Its primary mission was said to be "process development" and "production engineering." Brilliant scientists came to work there from all over the country, including at least one future Nobel prize winner (Raymond Davis, Jr.) Dayton was said to have the highest number of patents of any city in the country, many of them presumably from Mound and Wright-Patterson Air Force Base nearby, the military's principal center for aerospace research.

In 1954 Mound switched from the production of polonium to research in tritium and plutonium. Tritium, the radioactive isotope of hydrogen, came to be seen as better than polonium for intensifying nuclear explosions. Though tritium only has a half-life of 12.5 years, it is extremely radioactive and carcinogenic if inhaled. The chemical structure of tritium is similar to that of hydrogen, which means when it enters water it bonds chemically and cannot be extracted. One of Mound's first advanced research projects was to replenish the tritium in warheads (necessary because of the short half-life) and then turn diluted tritium-laced gas into water for disposal. Later Mound built laboratories for tritium purification. (14)

Mound also began to fabricate spheres and capsules made of plutonium for use in hydrogen bombs. Plutonium is produced artificially by neutron bombardment of uranium and is perhaps the deadliest element on earth. Though it is not dangerous to touch in solid form, a tiny microscopic speck--one millionth of one gram--can be fatal if inhaled. If plutonium in water is ingested, it is usually discharged, but if the levels are high enough, it can concentrate near the bone surfaces and be carcinogenic. (A 2005 study claims that EPA standards for plutonium in water today are 100 times too weak.) (15) Mound also developed a reactor which used the highly radioactive element thorium. A storage pit for the thorium eventually began to emit dangerous radon gas, caused by the thorium decay. (16)

The main sites for processing radioactive materials at Mound were two upland areas known as Main Hill and the SM/PP Hill (where the Special Metallurgical and Plutonium Processing plants were) and a lowland area known as Test Fire Valley. The R building, one of the original structures built in 1948, had a "cold" side for research, and a "hot" side for processing radioactive materials. (It too was later known for its high levels of radon gas.) (17) The S Building, constructed in 1950, with thirteen later additions, was used for plutonium re-search. The T Building was the large five-story concrete structure built into the hill. Originally Polonium-210 was purified there, but later the building was the site for tritium research. The T Building seems to have been designed as a kind of giant bomb-shelter, for it contained a water storage area to keep workers alive for several months in case of Russian attack. (18) According to a recent film on local Miamisburg history, army intelligence told Miamisburg officials in the 1950s that if Russia did launch an attack against the United States, Mound would be one of its first five targets. The whole Mound complex was surrounded by chained link fencing, razor wire and armed security guards. (19)

In 1954 two Mound scientists, John Birden and Ken Jordan, invented and patented the Radioisotopic Thermoelectric Generator (RTG), considered by some the most significant discovery made at Mound. The RTG converted heat from radiation to generate electricity. In 1959 the generator was given the new acronym SNAP to stand for System for Nuclear Auxiliary Power, and became part of the design for spacecraft. A Plutonium-238 capsule produced heat which was then converted into electricity, and this electrical power operated the instruments and radios. Plutonium-238 is not as radioactive as Plutonium-239 (the material which is used in bombs), but having a shorter half life (of 87 years) it is 280 times hotter. In 1961 the SNAP was used in a Navy navigation satellite in space. (20)

Though many Mound workers and Dayton residents today are proud of the contribution of the RTG to the space program, its history has a darker side. On April 21, 1964 a SNAP-9A-powered satellite failed to reach orbital velocity and re-entered the atmosphere 150,000 feet above the Indian Ocean. The SNAP-9A generator containing Plutonium-238 disintegrated on re-entry and vaporized 2.1 pounds of plutonium into the atmosphere. This amount does not sound like much, but given the fact that a microscopic particle can be deadly, it was. A group of European health and radiation protection agencies said a worldwide soil sampling carried out in 1970 showed SNAP-9A debris was present on all continents and all latitudes. (21) NASA has said repeatedly that the satellite crash was not serious, that it affected people far less than the fallout from the bomb tests in the 1950s (which perhaps *were* the most harmful artificial radia-tion Americans have been exposed to so far), but Dr. John Gofman, a Univer-sity of California biologist--who had worked on the Manhattan Project but later became a strong opponent of both nuclear power and nuclear weapons--said that the 1964 SNAP-9A accident *was* important, and may have been a factor in the rise in lung cancers in the 1970s. (22) There were also later accidents of spacecraft with plutonium on board. When Apollo 13 landed in the ocean near New Zealand, its RTG with eight pounds of plutonium did not disintegrate (as SNAP-9A had done), but it was never recovered and the canister is still lodged in the Tonga Trench of the Pacific Ocean, where it will be radioactive for the next 2,000 years. (23)

Despite the space accidents, Mound's work on the plutonium generators continued. On July 4, 1966 Monsanto put a large ad in the *New York Times* advertising for chemists, engineers, physicists and metallurgists to continue its military and space research. One scientist hired then said many years later, "It was a great place to work. The work was so challenging. Management supported people. A lot of us spent most of our careers there." (24) By the 1960s there were about 1,800 employees. The SNAP generator continued to be refined, and was used in the Pioneer space flights in the 1970s. SNAP-27 was later taken by the Apollo astronauts to the moon; in fact a fuel capsule of eight pounds of Plutonium-238 was left on the moon's surface, where it continued to generate electricity for the instruments to send information back to earth. (25) Mound scientists were also involved in other civilian and military research projects--supplying isotopes for medical and agricultural research, devising surveillance equipment for nuclear sites, as well as plutonium-powered batteries for artificial hearts. (26)

iii

Despite the concentration of brilliant scientific talent, and what one local newspaper called, the "serene perfection in safety and engineering that characterizes Mound Laboratory's annual environmental reports," (27) accidents did happen at Mound, and often they were serious. In fact, the main concern of activists who live near all the nuclear sites today is the extent to which accidental releases of radiation have contaminated the air, land and water, and endangered the health of workers and residents. In 1954 there was a spill in the R Building of the radioactive element actinium, which officials responded to by covering the cement floor with a slab of concrete. Forty years later during the cleanup of the R building, workers were not told about this spill and were contaminated by the actinium residue. (28) In 1964 a chemist named William Flint was exposed to Plutonium-235 when workers were changing filters; the monitor which was supposed to warn of high radioactive levels had been disconnected. Flint received an exposure of 100 rems at the time when 5 rems per year for workers was the limit. Years later he suffered health problems, including prostate cancer. In 2001 he was contacted by scientists at Los Alamos, asking if he would leave them his body when he died, but he had replied, "Why can't you examine me now?" (29) A study done in the 1980s discovered evidence that at least 90 employees over the years had received plutonium doses exceeding the federal standards. (30)

The most serious accident at Mound occurred in 1969. Highly contaminated waste from the Plutonium Processing plant was transferred to a waste processing plant by way of underground pipes. In 1969 one of these underground pipes ruptured and waste containing seven radionuclides, including plutonium, was released. Heavy rains during the next few days washed the contaminated soil into a bed of the Old Miami-Erie Canal, where 1/3 gram of plutonium was spread over about 1½ miles. The canal ran beside the Miamisburg Community Park which had a community swimming pool. (31) The most significant thing about this story is that the plutonium contamination in the canal bed wasn't discovered *for another five years.* In May, 1974 a tiny article appeared in the *New York Times* about the ruptured pipe. Richard Flitcraft, then director of the lab, said the material represented no health problems because "it was in the sediment and under water." (32) The area continued to be monitored, however. Several scientists said that they really didn't have enough data to assess how much danger there was. (33) For the next fifteen years Mound authorities assured Miamisburg residents that the area was safe, but in the 1990s, when some workers were repairing a railroad trestle near the old canal site--not knowing about the ruptured plutonium pipe--they were stopped and tested for contamination. Nothing was found in the workers, but residents who lived near the canal were told not to dig any wells. (34)

In the late 1960s Mound officials discovered an extensive amount of plutonium contamination in the Special Metallurgical building located on the crest of the hill. Soon thereafter decontamination workers in white suits and respirators began to remove ceilings, walls, pipes and floors, sending the contaminated material for temporary storage to Oak Ridge, Tennessee. The work was slow: excavating only four small tanks filled with radioactive waste took seven months and cost several million dollars. In 1972 a delay in the cleanup occurred when scientists discovered that plutonium had been absorbed into the very structure of the building;· they decided then to tear the whole building down. This process took another 16 years. To clean up and decontaminate this one building (built in five months for one million dollars) eventually took more than $57 million dollars and 29 years. From the 1970s onward, in fact, more and more of the Mound budget went for "D & D"--decommissioning and decontamination--of buildings in which the radiation levels were high. (35)

As will be seen in the stories of the other nuclear plants, officials at Mound in the early years found the easiest way of disposing of liquid radioactive waste was draining it into the river. For many years the Great Miami River served as a flushing agent for the radioactive and chemical contaminants at Mound. As much as 600,000 gallons of wastewater were released into the river every day. According to the recent study *Danger Lurks Below: The Threat to Major Water Supplies from the US DOE Nuclear Weapons Plants*, several radioactive elements had been deliberately dumped into the river (Protactinium-231, Thorium-230, and Thorium-232). (36) All have half-lives of billions of years. There was also all the tritium. As said before, it reacts with oxygen to form water, just as hydrogen does, and as tritium oxide (HTO) or tritiated water, can easily enter the living cells of plants, animals and human beings. According to *Danger Lurks Below,* tritiated wastewater at Mound was diluted, discharged into the surface water, and then released into the Great Miami River until 1970. (37) The EPA says that tritium is not as dangerous as other radionuclides because it leaves the body quickly, but an Alliance for Nuclear Accountability fact sheet says it stays in the body about 10 days, just as water does, and may become part of the cells' composition. Tritium has been linked to cancer, developmental and reproductive problems, and genetic disorders. (38) Throughout the 1960s and early 1970s the Atomic Energy Commission maintained that the tritium levels in the water of the Great Miami Aquifer beneath the plant were safe, but when the EPA was formed in 1976 it instituted much stricter standards; it said the tritium levels were *not* safe. The plant had to lower the water in the aquifer by pumping water from two wells, causing more river water to flow in to dilute the tritium. It also got rid of the underground waste transfer pipes and replaced the old dump with a lined sanitary landfill. (39) Eventually the water met EPA standards, but there's no way to know the effect of the tritiated water on the residents of the Great Miami Valley in the early years.

By the 1970s scientists throughout the country had become aware they had a huge problem on their hands as to what to do with all the radioactive waste which had accumulated during the years of heavy bomb production. Since there is no way to make radioactive material less radioactive, what does one do with it, how does one "dispose" of it? At Mound scientists began to experiment with a new process, developed at the Brookhaven National Laboratory, to solidify the tritiated water into concrete. (Possibly the same, or a similar process, was used as part of the cleanup at Maxey Flats, which will be discussed later.) The solidification didn't make the waste less radioactive, but put it in a form which prevented "migration." Solidification was not a perfect solution to the waste problem, however, for the huge blocks of concrete consumed a great deal of space at disposal sites. There were also questions as to how long the concrete itself would remain stable. (40)

iv

In December, 1977, over 30 years after the nuclear age had begun, the Department of Energy announced that it was hiring Dr. George Voelz to investigate causes of death in former plutonium workers at Rocky Flats, Hanford, Savannah River, Los Alamos, Oak Ridge and Mound. Stories of workers dying from leukemia and unusual cancers had become widespread. According to the *New York Times,* Voelz planned to contact workers at the plants for their occupational and health hazard records. Voelz, however, was a Los Alamos physicist and long-time DOE employee, not an independent investigator. There was also the problem, which Voelz himself acknowledged, that worker records had often not been accurately or truthfully maintained. (41) Thirteen years later the DOE refused to release the data of the Voelz study, apparently because at some places--particularly Hanford, Savannah River and Oak Ridge--the cancer rates were so high. The trustees of the Three Mile Island Public Fund, however, led by British epidemiologist Alice Stewart, sued the DOE to get the data--and eventually won. (42)

The results of the first Mound health study were not conclusive. One mortality study of Mound workers conducted by Voelz had concentrated exclusively on exposure to Polonium-210 and concluded that for 1944-1972 there was no evidence of excessive mortality. In analyzing this study, however, Robert Alvarez said the focus had been much too narrow, since Mound workers had been exposed to multiple radionuclides, such as Plutonium-238 and tritium, as well as Polonium-210. (43) Another DOE study done of workers at Mound showed an elevated rate for leukemia, though no specific causal relationship between exposure and disease could be established. (44) Epidemiological studies are extremely difficult to do in the nuclear field, as we shall see, because dose exposures are difficult to determine, pathways are hard to document, and the precise synergistic effects of radiation, toxic chemicals, and other personal and environmental factors are not easy to untangle. Cancers--and other diseases--also often have long latency periods, so the relationship of exposure to later illness cannot always be established. Furthermore, a crucial point is that some scientists also now believe that long-term radiation exposures at *low* levels may perhaps be even more dangerous than high-level exposures, since they may cause cell damage and damage to the immune system, so the ability of people to fight off *any* disease can be diminished. (45) After fifty years scientific understanding of the effects of radiation on human health is still far from complete.

In the 1990s workers suffering from a variety of cancers and other illnesses filed a class action lawsuit against the operators of Mound, based on the inadequacy of worker protection. The workers said they had been given little specific information about the danger of the radioactive materials they were handling. A former electrician at the plant testified at a hearing conducted by Senator Mike DeWine in 2002 that workers through the years had been improperly tested for radiation exposure and not tested for beryllium exposure at all (beryllium is highly toxic and can badly damage the lungs). (46) Many exposures were not measured, and there was no way to determine the true radiation doses the workers received. Gary Nolley, a union leader diagnosed with cancer, said that he had worked at the plant for 18 years without being tested for some of the radioactive substances.(47) For the next ten years, Mound workers, like those at the other nuclear sites, were involved in litigation against the plant operators, but with little success. They also sought compensation from the federal government, but were told they had to "prove" their cancers were at least 50% "caused by work conditions," something extremely difficult to do. According to an extensive study of area nuclear sites which appeared in the *Dayton Daily News* in November, 2006, only 133 of the 1,109 Mound health claims submitted to the federal government have been approved. One worker, Sherrie Neff, who began work at Mound in 1967 and was given little to protect her from radiation exposure, has since had four major cancer surgeries, and, recently, a leg and a lung removed, but all of her attempts to receive compensation have failed. She has been told repeatedly that she has been unable to "prove" her case. (48) (In the spring of 2007 neighbors were holding auction fundraisers for her, since her medical insurance had run out.) (49)

In 2006 Sanford Cohen and Associates did an independent audit of the Mound site, talking to 17 workers, raising questions about the DOE's "site profile" and its position that the plant had not seriously contributed to worker illnesses. According to this audit, workers had many legitimate reasons for viewing the government data with skepticism. Those interviewed said that many workers had not been properly monitored for possible exposures to high levels of radon gas and superheated Plutonium-238 oxide, which linger in the lungs and do not show up in urine tests; that though "radiation workers" had been required to wear film badges, many others--administrators, secretaries, maintenance and janitorial staffs--had not; that Mound officials ignored film badges which were completely "black," due to excessive exposure, saying that they were sure that workers had "intentionally" blackened them in order to get out of hazardous duties; that Mound research involved a lot of "exotic isotopes" which weren't always a part of the monitoring; many were ubiquitous and moved all over the site. (50) Workers hope this new data can be used in future compensation claims.

In the 1980s residents who lived near Mound, like the workers, began to wonder if accidents and releases from the plant could have contributed to *their* health problems. (Abnormal growths on the skin were so common that the residents called them "Mound cysts.") (51) A Miamisburg resident, Sharon Cowdrey, whose son had died of leukemia, was one of the founders of MESH (Miamisburg Environmental Safety and Health). A nurse, she was to become an eloquent advocate in the coming years for community involvement in environmental decisions. Some of the other early members of MESH, primarily women, had also lost family members to cancer. For the next 20 years MESH monitored the activities of the plant and confronted government officials about discrepancies in official statements and reports.

In the 1990s the ATSDR (Agency for Toxic Substances and Disease Registry), part of the Center for Disease Control in Atlanta, agreed to conduct a health assessment of the Miamisburg area. After considering plant emissions (from plant records), cancer data (but not the data for other diseases), worker studies (again with plant data) and some interviews, the ATSDR concluded that there were "*no apparent* [italics added] health hazards" in the Mound area. The report said that the only dangerous incident had occurred in 1982-83 when releases from Mound's sanitary sewage treatment facility went into the Great Miami River, proving a "temporary" hazard to people swimming, boating, and fishing in the river.(52) The report said the residents were in no danger from the radiation.

The complete version of the ATSDR report can be found online (www.atsdr.cdc.gov). It includes the transcript of a hearing where about 200 residents were allowed to ask questions and express their concerns. The overwhelming majority of the questions had to do with the illnesses residents saw or were experiencing: cancer clusters on certain streets and in certain neighborhoods, unusual tumors, leukemia, the dying of trees and animals near the plant. To almost every question, the panel answered automatically that the radiation releases from Mound had not been sufficient to cause any illness or problem. Asked about the high number of cancers in Miamisburg, the panel simply quoted the National Cancer Institute, that the high rates of cancer in America are caused by smoking and bad diet. The panel did acknowledge that the number of lung cancers in Montgomery County, where Miamisburg is located, was higher than that of any county in Ohio (and also higher than the national average), but they said there was no way to prove the lung cancers were related in any way to the radioactive emissions from Mound. Someone asked why the scientists hadn't gone house-to-house to acquire more data. The panel said they didn't regard such surveys an efficient use of their time, once they figured out the exposure levels--from the plant data--did not indicate any particular danger. Residents were left with a weird sense of disconnect between the ATSDR report and their own illnesses. Once when Mound officials offered to test the well water of Teresa Strepp, one of the nearby residents, she said, "I'm sorry, but I don't take your word for something you test." Her husband James was even more emphatic. "We've been lied to too long to believe anything they tell us."(53) Today the residents near Mound are still seeking compensation, and are being represented in their court case by the firm of Cincinnati attorney Stanley Chesley, who won the compensation case for the residents near Fernald. (54)

v

In 1988 a company called EG&G, an engineering firm with long connections to the Pentagon, replaced Monsanto as operators of the plant. The expensive dismantling of the buildings contaminated by the plutonium continued. In 1988 the Department of Energy first talked about the possibility of closing Mound, because, they said, the government was beginning to "re-conceptualize" its nuclear program, closing some of the contaminated sites, consolidating others, building new ones. (55) Serious problems, though, at Mound continued. On November 9, 1989 workers conducting a secret experiment with a laser beam shattered a quartz window and released 3.7 grams of tritium gas. The tritium went up an unfiltered smokestack into the atmosphere and two hundred workers had to be evacuated from the plant. Mound authorities gave conflicting reports as to how much the public may have been exposed to, though they assured the press there was no danger. Dan Reicher of the National Resources Defense Council, however, which monitored the plant, said it was about seven times the amount released in the whole of a previous *year*. (56) The accident caused the tritium testing at Mound to be suspended. An official at the Nuclear Control Institute said the accident had given EG&G a "black eye." "They are considered the best tritium-handling facility in the nuclear weapons complex. Somebody really screwed up." (57) EG&G was also penalized the following year when it was discovered that some of the urine of the actinium cleanup workers had been left on a shelf for two years and never tested. (58)

In September, 1990 a Department of Energy "tiger team" of contamination specialists visited Mound. Though an EG&G official said, "There is absolutely nothing wrong with Mound's safety record, its environmental record or anything like that," the tiger team found Mound guilty of 77 environmental, health and safety deficiencies, which they said would cost $140 million to correct. (59) Mound was added to the National Priorities List and designated a Superfund site--at about the same time this was happening at Fernald, Piketon, Maxey Flats and Paducah. The EPA and Department of Energy signed an agreement to "remediate" the Mound site, that is, bring it up to certain environmental standards. BWX Technologies, formerly Babcock and Wilcox, was contracted for the remediation work.

Rumors about the plant closing persisted. Shirley Coleman, whose father had come from Nebraska in the forties as a construction worker to help build

Mound, lamented the possible closing in her Koffee Kup restaurant, where workers for years had come by for breakfast and lunch. (60) In April, 1992 a large "Save the Mound" rally was held, attended by hundreds of people, many Mound employees. Senator John Glenn, speaking as an advocate for the workers, said he would fight to keep it open. The mayor of Miamisburg said he had petitions which he planned to take to the President. Crystal Burns of MESH said, "We don't want the workers to lose their jobs. We just want the contamination cleaned up." (61)

As part of the Superfund cleanup agreement, four areas near Mound were designated as needing immediate remediation. The first one was the Great Miami Aquifer, which was badly contaminated with toxic chemicals from a closed landfill and a waste disposal building. The second problem was an area to the north of the plant where springs contaminated both with chemicals and tritiated water were seeping out of slopes. There were also seventy-three different, smaller sites throughout the plant which had radioactive and chemical contamination. Finally there was also the Old Miami-Erie Canal, where the plutonium pipe had ruptured, which would have to be excavated and the contaminated soil put in boxes and shipped offsite. (62)

Cleaning up the aquifer involved treating the water to get rid of the chemical contaminants. Mound employed a "pump-and-treat" system where water was pumped out of the aquifer, treated, then re-injected. Though getting rid of the toxic chemicals, this method did not get rid of plutonium, tritium or other radionuclides. (63) Another part of the cleanup involved digging up the plutonium-contaminated soil from throughout the plant site (20,000 cubic yards of it) and shipping it for temporary storage to Idaho Falls (until Idaho temporarily banned it.) (64)   For a time after that, Mound stored the plutonium-contaminated soil in containers on-site. Remediation also finally began on the canal area where the pipe had ruptured. Contamination had been found in the one mile strip closest to the spill at high levels; it had also seeped five to ten feet into the soil. The U.S. EPA, the Ohio EPA, the city of Miamisburg, and two community groups, Neighbors in Need and MESH, worked together to establish cleanup standards. MESH objected to the first proposed EPA cleanup level, got it reduced by half, and then half again. The canal cleanup was completed in 1998 at a cost of $48 million. (65)

In the 1990s Mound's plutonium-generated space vehicles were back in the news. Two of the space shuttles carried satellites on board powered by the RTG. In both instances activists tried in the courts to stop the flights, but failed. In 1996 when NASA announced plans to launch the Cassini satellite to explore Saturn, writer Karl Grossman discovered that 72.3 pounds of Plutonium-238 would be used. NASA planned to send Cassini back to earth for a "swingby" to give it the velocity to get to Saturn, buzzing the earth at 42,300 mph and at a height of 312 miles. If Cassini came too close to earth during this "slingshot" maneuver and there was an "inadvertent re-entry," Grossman feared the craft could break up and rain plutonium all over the earth's surface. The environmental impact study, which Grossman eventually acquired from NASA, even acknowledged this risk. (66) In May, 1996 several thousand people demonstrated at Cape Canaveral to protest the swingby. At another rally the following year one of the speakers was a 30-year NASA employee who had once been in charge of emergency preparedness. "They call the RTGs indestructible," he said. "They're indestructible just like the Titanic was unsinkable. And they are committing the lie, the sin of omission, in not telling you the whole truth. There should be public hearings." (67) Because of the protests, NASA did move the swingby out to 500 miles, but still went ahead with the launch.

vi

In 1993 it was announced that Mound would definitely close. The Department of Energy gave Miamisburg $200,000 to begin work on new plans for the site, once the decommissioning was complete and the land was ostensibly "cleaned up." Miamisburg was told that the site would not be safe for residential use, but could be used for industry. (That it was not safe for residences was perhaps related to the fact that children are particularly susceptible to radiation exposure.) Governor George Voinovich came to Mound and spoke to officials and workers in remarks which were broadcast throughout the whole complex. He promised the state would do whatever it could to keep "the wonderful work force" in the area. (68) Local and even some international businessmen were invited to investigate the location. One Mound official said, on the day of an open house, that it was "mind-boggling for a federal employee to see all these uncleared people." (69) What was even more mind-boggling for some had been the arrival in 1992 of some Russian scientists, there to investigate the steel containers (Mound-designed) for shipping Plutonium-238, which the U.S. had just purchased from the former Soviet Union. (70)

In 1998, in a complex business arrangement, the details of which were not made public, the DOE sold all of the Mound plant (for ten dollars) to the Miamisburg Mound Community Improvement Corporation (MMCIC). In 1997 Congressman Tony Hall of Dayton introduced a bill to cut the liability of businesses to encourage them to relocate at the old Mound site. (71) Like the Price-Anderson Act, which insures that nuclear power plants have limited financial responsibility in case of a catastrophe, the Tony Hall bill was an acknowledgement, that, for all the talk about cleanup, the Department of Energy itself wasn't sure what things would be like when the cleanup was over, or what new problems might emerge. The MMCIC formed a private industrial park, Mound Advanced Technology Center, which eventually had about 20 companies with 200 employees--engineering firms, laboratories, shops for precision equipment. Many were owned and operated by former Mound scientists; many had research contracts with the federal government. (72) Scientists in a DOE oversight committee expressed some concern that the DOE had perhaps rushed into the commercialization of Mound too quickly, before clearly identifying all the hazards and contaminants onsite, or assessing the possibility of any accidental release of radiation, but no information exists at this time as to whether or not there is evidence of any problems. (73)

Research on the Radioisotopic Thermal Generator (RTG) remained at Mound within the Advanced Technology Center, possibly as a concession to local officials who wanted to keep some of the Mound work in the area. After 9/11, however, the Department of Energy announced it would move *all* the Mound nuclear research to the Argonne National Laboratory-West at Idaho Falls, supposedly to consolidate operations and save security costs. (74) Some workers in Dayton regretted this decision--and so, for different reasons, did some people in Idaho. The Snake River Alliance, located in Boise, issued a statement saying that they didn't want the "plutonium space batteries" coming there for business. The Snake River Aquifer, the second largest unified aquifer in the country, is already contaminated with plutonium because of careless disposal of wastes from the Rocky Flats plant near Denver, shut down due to extensive contamination in 1989. (75)

vii

Mound's original plan was to have the remediation finished by 2010, but when the federal government began to cut funding for all the nuclear cleanups, local officials feared it might never be completed. As a solution to the problem, the Department of Energy proposed a "fast-track" cleanup plan (similar to one also proposed for Fernald). A new company, CH2M Hill, was given a $314 million contract to oversee the Accelerated Cleanup Program to get the site ready for business by 2006. CH2M Hill immediately began to demolish buildings and remove contaminated soil and objects. The company was told it would get a multi-million dollar bonus if it made the new deadline. The reason for the accelerated operation was ostensibly economics--$100 million could be saved-- (76) but the rush to meet the deadline at Mound and get the bonuses, as at Fernald, led to some questionable practices. For instance, in 2001 Mound got a special exemption from the DOE to send its plutonium-contaminated waste to Savannah River in South Carolina for temporary storage. This dangerous, unnecessary transfer was simply because Mound wanted to say its site was "clean." Savannah River accepted the waste in order "to accelerate the closure date of the Mound site," i.e., help the remediators get their bonus. (77)

By the summer of 2006 the most dangerous Mound waste had left or would be leaving Savannah River to go to the new underground Waste Isolation Pilot Project (WIPP) in Carlsbad, New Mexico, where it will permanently remain. WIPP is the designated site for all the transuranic waste created at the nuclear weapons production plants since the 1940s. (Transuranic elements are those artificially-created elements, such as plutonium, which have a heavier weight than uranium, the heaviest natural element; they are extremely radioactive and toxic, with half-lives sometimes of millions or billions of years). The transuranic waste brought to WIPP over the next 35 years will be stored in lead-lined barrels in salt chambers deep within the earth. It is hoped that eventually the salt will encase the waste in a solid block where it will remain, supposedly safely, for 10,000 years. WIPP has long been opposed by some of the citizens of New Mexico, however, particularly the Southwest Research and Information Center, because of the geological instability of the site. Even if there are no ecological or engineering problems before the enclosure is completed, there are no guarantees that the materials will not leak at some time in the millions of years the barrels will be enclosed. WIPP is located in the midst of large quantities of oil and natural gas; there is the possibility that some form of mining a hundred, a thousand, a hundred thousand years from now could cause a catastrophic release of radiation then.

Despite all the demolition going on at Mound, in 1997 a new $10 million facility was opened in the T Building, TERF (Tritium Emissions Radiation Facility). Mound had been processing tritium with a system of pipes which went back to the 1960s. The new system, officials said, would increase the safety and capability of the system to collect and dispose of tritium. The older system had had the potential for an accidental release of 10,000 to 50,000 units of tritium (when 100 was the acceptable limit) and the new system would limit the risk to 200. While the numbers are reassuring about TERF, they raise questions about emissions in the early years. (78) In 1998 when the last barrel of tritium was sent to Savannah River, there was a celebration at the plant and in the community. Even the mayor of Miamisburg said, "Just think, seven years ago, we were fighting to keep this here."(79) When the tritium cleanup was over, the TERF building itself was decontaminated and torn down.

A recent report of the Nuclear Information and Resource Service (NIRS) has expressed concern that some of the radioactive waste from Mound (and the other weapons production sites) may have ended up illegally in landfills in other parts of the state. For instance, the Industrial Excess Landfill in Uniontown, Ohio, which was not licensed or regulated for radioactivity, has shown high levels of Plutonium-238, which may have come from Mound. (80) There really are no precise records *where* all the nuclear waste from the DOE sites has gone over the years, which means there may be pockets of radioactive contamination in landfills all over, which the public is simply not aware of.

Early on in the cleanup process CH2M Hill made an unexpected discovery of a new danger at a site location known as OU-1. In digging the soil to install the pump-and- treat mechanism for the aquifer, the contractors had discovered a cache of smashed drums contaminated with thorium. (81) Like uranium, thorium decays into dangerous "daughter" products, the most significant being Radium-228, which is deadly. CH2M Hill realized that cleaning up OU-l would be dangerous, time-consuming and expensive, so initially proposed that the waste be left where it was, entombed in an engineered barrier, a proposal which the DOE, EPA and state of Ohio at first went along with. The city of Miamisburg, however, didn't like the idea and demanded that the waste be dug up and removed. CH2M then said that OU-l was not part of its original cleanup contract, so wanted no part in its removal. (Perhaps it also wanted to make the closing by the 2006 deadline to get the bonus.) The DOE finally agreed and on August 1, 2006, CH2M Hill declared the site "clean," subject to DOE review of their final report. (82) Rep. David Hobson of Ohio, who chaired the sub-committee which funded the DOE, managed to add another $34 million to the energy and water appropriations bill for 2007 to pay *someone else* to clean up OU-1. (Accelerated Remediation Company LLC, known as ARC, received the contract in October, 2006.)

In the fall of 2007 the contractors said they had run out of money. Even though the cleanup wasn't complete, the DOE wanted to stop work on the site, a proposal which raised an outcry from the officials at the Mound Advanced Technology Center, who knew they might have difficulty attracting new tenants to a still-contaminated site. (83) In March, 2008, the Senate budget committee, prompted by Senator Sherrod Brown, approved money for the completion of the cleanup. (84)

viii

The DOE is scheduled to turn the Mound site over to its Office of Legacy Management, which will supervise the long-term stewardship. The Miamisburg Mound Community Development Corporation (MMCIC) has been designated steward for its part of the site. Plans are being formed for the LSO (Local Stockholder Organization) which will monitor the site for the community at large. At an Alliance for Nuclear Accountability panel in the fall of 2005, Sharon Cowdrey said that, even though there are some people in Miamisburg who want to forget that the hill was once a nuclear plant, there are many others who do not. When a community coalition sent out a four-page health survey to all residents of Miamisburg, they immediately received 4,000 responses. (85)

The workers struggling to receive compensation for their illnesses received startling information in 2007, when it was revealed that in 1993 Mound had sent 458 boxes of records to Los Alamos to be "de-contaminated." For several years they had been stored outdoors in large transportainers. In 2003 forty of those boxes had been returned to Mound and decontaminated for use in the dose re-construction claims, but the rest, the staff of Los Alamos decided, were too expensive to decontaminate, so were simply buried in an underground landfill. (86) Workers and worker advocates were incensed by this news. Richard Miller of the Government Accountability Project said, "The fact that these records were hot tells you something about working conditions where those records were kept." (87) The greater question is whether those records should have been buried at all. The DOE maintains it did nothing wrong, that the records did not pertain to health matters, but even a Los Alamos official admitted, "It is difficult to evaluate the value of the records in an exact manner." (88) Among the thousands of records buried were Mound studies of the properties of toxic chemicals which were used, and a description of the 1989 accident when tritium had been released. (89) At this time, workers are trying to get those records exhumed and decontaminated, though given the cost--in the millions--their efforts may not be successful, and the medical questions of both workers and residents may never be answered. In September, 2007 NIOSH agreed to hear a new petition that the Mound workers be given "special cohort status," which means they will not have to submit extensive proof of cancer causation in order to receive compensation. The former Mound supervisor who submitted the petition admitted that plant records had consistently been flawed or incomplete. (90)

In 1985 he had asked NASA to tell him the odds of a catastrophic shuttle accident, and they said 1 in 100,000. After Challenger 1 blew up in January, 1986 (it did not have plutonium on board), the odds changed considerably to 1 in 76. In 2003 the explosion of the Columbia Shuttle increased the odds again. (91) On January 19, 2006 an unmanned spacecraft called New Horizons was launched toward Pluto with 24 pounds of plutonium on board. Knowing there was a 1 in 300 chance of an accident, activists again tried to stop the launch, but failed. (92) In the summer of 2006, however, NASA announced its intention of using solar power in the future to fuel deep space explorations rather than nuclear generators. (93)

Activists are still concerned, though, that much of the plutonium now being processed at the Idaho National Laboratory--reportedly to be used once again for secret unspecified "national security purposes"--will again cause workers and residents to be exposed to accidental releases of radiation. The danger has not gone away; it has simply been moved. Pluto in classical mythology was the god of the underworld, the god of death. Allen Ginsberg, in his "Plutonian Ode," refers to plutonium as "the new element, unborn in nature.....Delusion of metal empires!" What seems to be happening at all the nuclear sites--Mound, Idaho and elsewhere--is the growing awareness of the threats of the "metal empire" to the cells of life itself.

Notes: Mound

1. "A History of Mound," *Dayton Daily News,* August 8, 1993, 4E.

2. DeBrosse, Jim, "The Dayton Project," *Dayton Daily News,* December 5, 2004, A1.

3. DeBrosse, Jim, "Manhattan Project Worker to Discuss Bomb," *Dayton Daily News,* March 20, 2006, B1.

4. "The Dayton Sites," *Ohio EPA Report. Office of Federanl Facilities Oversight.* (http://offo2.epa.state.oh.us/doe/fusrap/Dayton/Dayton_sites.htm)

5. Oziewicz, Estanislao, "Polonium is Costly, Undetectable, Trillion Times More Toxic than Cyanide," *The Globe and Mail* (Canada), December 2, 2006, A23.

6. Gerson, Joseph, *Empire and the Bomb: How the US Uses Nuclear Weapons to Dominate the World* (Ann Arbor: Pluto Press, 2007), 11-38.

7. Rhodes, Richard, *The Making of the Atomic Bomb* (New York: Simon and Schuster, 1986), 752, 769.

8. Caufield, Catherine, *Multiple Exposures: Chronicles of the Radiation Age* (New York: Harper and Row, 1989), 62.

9. Light, Esther, *Miamisburg, the First 150 Years* (Miamisburg: Miamisburg Women's Club, 1968), 19, 23, 83.

10. "A History of Mound" 4E.

11. "A History of Mound" 4E.

12. Beyerlein, Tom, "Daughter Peels Layers of Secrecy from Mound Worker's Death," *Dayton Daily News,* November 13, 2006.

13. Cox, Phyllis, "Miamisburg Prepares to Take Over Mound Utilities," *Dayton Daily News,* March 25, 2004, Z8-7.

14. "Precious Waste: Environment, Industry Profit from Tritium Recycling," *Dayton Daily News,* August 8, 1993, 4E.

15. "EPA Drinking Water Standard for Plutonium is 100 Times Too Weak." Institute for Energy and Environmental Research Press Release, August 3, 2005. (www.ieer.org/reports/badtothebone/pressrel/html)

16. Beyerlein, Tom, "Audit Says Many Mound Workers Likely Exposed to Toxins, *Dayton Daily News,* January 28, 2007, A14.

17. Beyerlein, "Audit Says."

18. Dempsey, Dale, "Mound Unveils Plant," *Dayton Daily News,* January 14, 1997, 1A.

19. Film: *Miamisburg: The One and Only.* [Ohio], 1999.

20. McElheny, Victor K. "Plutonium Power for Space Exploration," *New York Times,* August 31, 1977, 68.

21. Grossman, Karl, *The Wrong Stuff: The Space Program's Nuclear Threat to Our Planet* (Monroe, MI: Common Courage Press, 2005), 11-13.

22. Film: *Arsenal of Hypocrisy: The Space Program and the Military Industrial Complex.* Produced by Randy Atkins. Available from Global Network Against Weapons and Nuclear Power in Space. (www.space4peace.com)

23. Grossman, Karl and Judith Long, "Apollo Outtakes," *The Nation,* September 11, 1995.

24. McNutt, Randy, "Cold War Days," *Cincinnati Enquirer,* May 6, 2000, 3B.

25. Smithsonian National Air and Space Museum Website. (www.nasm.si.edu)

26. "A History of Mound" 4E.

27. "Radiation Leak May Have Been Going on for 16 Years," *Cincinnati Post,* May 17, 1974, 21.

28. Hannah, James, "Mound Workers Seek Inquiry; Suit Alleges They Weren't Told of Radiation Exposure," *Cleveland Plain Dealer,* August 17, 1995, 6B.

29. Dempsey, Dale, "Feds Close to Aiding Nuclear Workers." *Dayton Daily News,* January 12, 2000, 1B.

30. Coyle, D. and L. Finaldi, E. Greenfield, M. Hamilton, E. Hedemann, W. McDonnell, M.Resnikoff, J. Scarlott and J. Tichenor, *Deadly Defense: Military Radioactive Landfills. A Citizen's Guide* (New York: Radioactive Waste Campaign, 1988), 66.

31. Coyle 66.

32. "Radioactive Matter Found In Ohio Canal," *New York Times,* May 15, 1974, 48.

33. "Study Finds No Present Peril from Plutonium Spill," *Cincinnati Enquirer,* May 18, 1976, D1.

34. Sikora, Mary, "New Fears About Pollution," *Dayton Daily News,* May 13, 1991, 1A.

35. Schneider, Keith, "The 29-Year Ordeal to Tear Down One Building," *New York Times,* October 31, 1988, A14.

36. Radioactive Waste Management Associates, *Danger Lurks Below: The Threat to Major Water Suppliers from the U.S. DOE Nuclear Weapons Plants* (Written for the Alliance for Nuclear Accountability, April, 2004), 103. (www.ananuclear.org)

37. Radioactive Waste Management 102.

38. "Tritium Production," Radioactive Pork Report 2004. Alliance for Nuclear Accountability. (www.ananuclear.org/tritium2005).

39. Coyle 66.

40. Jones, Stacy V., "Patents: Economical Disposal of Nuclear Wastes," *New York Times,* November 17, 1979, 30.

41. "Study is Begun on Effects of Plutonium on Workers," *New York Times,* December 13, 1977, 16.

42. "U.S. to Release Health Records on Nuclear Weapons Workers," *Dayton Daily News,* May 19, 1990, 8A.

43. Alvarez, Robert, "The Risks of Making Nuclear Weapons: A Review of the Health and Mortality Experience of DOE Workers." The Government Accountability Project. January, 2000. (www.downwinders.org/doe_worker_studies.htm)

44. Makhijani, Arjun, Howard Hu and Katherine Yih, eds., *Nuclear Wastelands: A Global Guide to Nuclear Weapons Production and Its Health and Environmental Effects* (Cambridge, Mass: MIT Press, 2000), 276.

45. "All Levels of Radiation Confirmed to Cause Cancer," Nuclear Information and Resource Center Press Release, June 30, 2005. (www.nirs.org/press/06-30-2005/1).

46. Welsh-Huggins, Andrew, "Panel Considers Radiation Compensation," *Cleveland Plain Dealer,* May 16, 2000, 2B.

47. Dillon, Jim, "Mound Employees File Class Action," *Dayton Daily News,* August 16, 1995, 3B.

48. Beyerlein, Tom and Lynn Hulsey, "Complicated Claims Process Often Ends in Rejections," *Dayton Daily News,* November 13, 2006.

49. "Neighbors Headline," *Dayton Daily News,* March 8, 2007, Z8-7.

50. Beyerlein, "Audit Shows."

51. Agency for Toxic Substances and Disease Registry Report on Mound Laboratory. (www.atsdr.cdc.gov/hac/pha/doemound/dmf_p2.html).

52. "Mound Plant No Hazard," *Dayton Daily News,* April 17, 1998, 6B.

53. Sikora, "New Fears" 1A.

54. "Mound Residents Case to Go to Trial," PR Newswire, August 18, 2007.

55. Schneider, Keith, "U.S. is Pessimistic on Reactors' Role in Atomic Arsenal," *New York Times,* December 27, 1988, A1.

56. Wald, Matthew L., "Tritium Released at a Weapons Lab," *New York Times,* November 9, 1989, A30.

57. Dougherty, John, "Mound's Leak Stalls Tests on U.S. Nukes," *Dayton Daily News,* February 17, 1990, 3A.

58. Gaffney, Timothy R., "Mound Workers Fearful: 24 Test Positive for '91 Radiation," *Dayton Daily News,* December 15, 1994, 1A.

59. Dillon, Jim, "Audit Counts 77 Health, Safety Flaws at Mound Site," *Dayton Daily News,* September 21, 1990, 1A.

60. Sikora, Mary, "Miamisburg Community, Schools Depend on Support from Plant," *Dayton Daily News,* January 1, 1992, Z2-1.

61. "Glenn Leads Mound Rally," *Dayton Daily News,* April 5, 1992, 1B.

62. Brinckman, Jonathan, "Cleanup Will Help Ease Impact of Closing," *Dayton Daily News,* May 28, 1993, 11A.

63. Radioactive Waste Management 106.

64. Barker, Rocky, "Cecil Andrus Knew How to Take a Stand," *High Country News* 27 *(*February 20, 1995). (www.hcn.org)

65. "Proposed Cleanup of South Fork of Acid Canyon: Reports on Other Sites." Concerned Citizens for Nuclear Safety (www.nuclear active.org/docs/acid canyon.html)

66. Grossman, Karl, "U.S. Slinging Plutonium into Space," *Cleveland Plain Dealer,* May 22, 1996.

67. Grossman, *The Wrong Stuff* 218.

68. "Voinovich Promises Help in Salvaging Mound Plant," *Cleveland Plain Dealer,* August 23, 1993, 3B.

69. Wallack, Todd R., "DOE's Boost to Town: $200K," *Dayton Daily News,* August 13, l993, 5B.

70. Gaffney, Tim, "Russian Technicians to Visit Mound Plant," *Dayton Daily News,* July 3, 1992, 3B.

71. Dempsey, Dale, "Mound Rebound: Once-Secret Weapons Plant Opens for Business," *Dayton Daily News,* March 4, 1998, 3B.

72. Dempsey, "Mound Rebound" 3B.

73. "The Committee's Observations at Mound and Fernald," *Long Term Stewardship of DOE Legacy Waste Sites: A Status Report (2003).* (http://darwin.nap.edu/books/ni000504/html/57.html)

74. Lippman, Thomas W., "Ohio Nuclear Weapons Plant Closing Delayed," *Washington Post,* March 17, 1993, A7.

75. Snake River Alliance Website. (www.snakeriveralliance.org/Pu238/plutonium.htm)

76. "DOE Tries Contractor Carrots to Accelerate Mound Cleanup," *Engineer-*

ing News-Record 249 (December 16, 2002), 13.

77. Savannah River Site. (http://sti.srs.gov/fulltext/ms2002902/ms2002902.html)

78. Dempsey, "Mound Unveils Plant" 1A.

79. "Nuclear Arms Era Over for Mound," *Dayton Daily News,* September 29, 1998, 5B.

80. D'Arrigo, Diane and Mary Olson, *Out of Control--on Purpose: DOE's Dispersal of Radioactive Waste into Landfills and Consumer Products* (Takoma Park: Nuclear Information and Resource Service, 2007), 48.

81. Site Closure Panel: Mound. Alliance for Nuclear Accountability Meeting. Cincinnati, Ohio. October 21, 2005.

82. Hansen, Brian, "With Cleanup at Mound Nearly Done, DOE Unveils Contract to Finish the Job," *Inside Energy,* August 7, 2006, 11.

83. Beyerlein, Tom, "Cost Overruns Halt Cleanup at Mound Plant," *Dayton Daily News,* November 18, 2007, A1.

84. Beyerlein, Tom, "Senate Panel Adds Funds for Mound, Piketon. *Dayton Daily News* March 9, 2008, A11

85. Site Closure Panel: Mound.

86. Beyerlein, Tom, "Former Mound Employees, Advocates Question Destruction of Records," *Dayton Daily News,* January 7, 2007, A15.

87. Beyerlein, "Former Mound."

88. Beyerlein, Tom, "Mound Plant Records Buried in New Mexico," *Dayton Daily News,* February 14, 2007, A4.

89. Beyerlein, "Mound Plant Records."

90. Beyerlein, Tom, "Agency to Review Worker's Request," *Dayton Daily News,* September 1, 2007, A4.

91. Grossman, Karl, "The Case Against the Plutonium Space Race," *Boise Weekly,* March 16, 2005.

92. "Contact NASA: No Plutonium Launch: Cancel New Horizons." Global Network against Weapons and Nuclear Power in Space. (www.space4peace.org)

93. Morring, Jr., Frank, "Far-Flung Arrays: Advances in Solar Cell Efficiency Enable Non-Nuclear Deep Space Robotic Explorers," *Aviation Week & Space Technology* 165 (July 17, 2006), 160.

THE HIDDEN PLUTONIUM:
PADUCAH GASEOUS
DIFFUSION PLANT,
PADUCAH, KENTUCKY

Paducah, Kentucky is 234 miles to the southwest of Cincinnati, further away than the other sites, but included here because its history is intimately connected to that of the other uranium enrichment plant at Piketon, Ohio, and because the nature of its contamination is so important to the nuclear story of the region. Much of the basic information in this narrative comes from two series of articles, one by Joby Warrick in the *Washington Post* in 1999, and the other by James R. Carroll and James Malone in the *Louisville Courier-Journal* in June, 2000. Warrick's story relies on some of the 2,000 pages of evidence collected by former radiation safety officers at Paducah who, with a former worker, filed a fraud law suit against the companies which had operated the plant; the Carroll/Malone stories rely on reports of Kentucky authorities, scientists, and residents.

Paducah is located in the southwestern corner of Kentucky near the confluence of the Ohio and Tennessee Rivers, only 25 miles from the point where the Ohio reaches the Mississippi. Chickasaw Indians once had hunting grounds in the area, but in the early 1800s signed treaties, ceded lands and moved south. It was General William Clark (of Lewis and Clark fame) who laid out the town of Paducah and named it after a legendary Chickasaw chief. The first European-

Americans arrived in the 1820s and the community grew as a river town. In the late 19th and early 20th century the greatest danger to the town was from the constant flooding of the Ohio River. The famous big flood of 1937--still remembered throughout the Ohio River Valley--caused considerable damage to Paducah, but the town rebuilt itself and put up a flood wall in 1946. Its population at the time was about 35,000. The writer Bobbie Ann Mason, who grew up in a small town 26 miles away, said that as a child in the forties, going to Paducah was a trip to the "big city": it had department stores, trains, and movie houses. (1)

During World War II Paducah had a defense plant, Kentucky Ordnance Works (called K.O.W. by the residents), a 1,400-acre site about 16 miles west of town, which manufactured TNT for conventional weapons. It was located about four miles south of the Ohio River. When it closed after the war, it left TNT residue, some of which is still in a fenced-off area of a nearby wildlife reserve. (2)

In the late 1930s and early 1940s physicists had discovered that it would not be easy to build a nuclear bomb because raw uranium ore had only 0.7% of the fissionable isotope U-235 needed for an explosion. Physicist Niels Bohr, in fact, was relieved by this fact in 1939, thinking that retrieving the U-235 would be too difficult and expensive for atom bomb-making to become a permanent enterprise. When he saw the massive 60,000-acre complex built at Oak Ridge, Tennessee in the early forties, however, he realized the American government (without taxpayer or congressional knowledge) had given the military unlimited funds. Bohr told Edward Teller, "I told you it couldn't be done without turning the whole country into a factory. You have done just that." (3) By the year 2000 there were thirteen major nuclear weapons production sites in the United States, covering a land area equal to that of Delaware and Rhode Island. (4)

Research at Oak Ridge was conducted on three different methods to extract, or "enrich," the U-235 for bombs: electromagnetic isotope separation, thermal diffusion and gaseous diffusion. Some research was also done on the centrifuge method, but very little. The isotope separation plant went into operation first, but General Leslie Groves, head of the Manhattan Project, preferred the faster gaseous diffusion method, evidently already thinking about its usefulness in large-scale bomb production after the war. A gigantic $20 million gaseous diffusion plant--known as K-25-- was built at Oak Ridge and operated for the government by Carbide and Carbon Chemicals (later Union Carbide). In early

1945 some uranium enriched at K-25 was sent on to the isotope separation plant for further enrichment, up to 97%, for the bomb later used on Hiroshima. (5)

The gaseous diffusion process was based on the principle that gaseous molecules of different atomic weight travel at different speeds. Uranium hexafluoride gas was forced through thousands of nickel "barriers" with microscopic holes to separate the U-235 from the heavier U-238. (U-238 is called "depleted uranium" because it cannot sustain a chain reaction, though it is still radioactive). The K-25 plant at Oak Ridge consisted of hundreds of miles of interconnected stages of piping. The whole operation of pipes, compressors and converters was known as a "cascade."

By August, 1950 Truman was already committed to expanding America's nuclear arsenal and was told by advisors that the Oak Ridge facilities were no longer sufficient. He made the decision to build a new gaseous diffusion plant, huge and expensive though he knew it would be. After considering eight possible sites, he finally selected Paducah, the hometown of his vice-president, Alben W. Barkley. October 18, 1950 the Kentucky Ordnance Works was officially selected as the site for the new gaseous diffusion plant. An additional 3,600 acres of land were purchased, so the facility as a whole covered about 5,000 acres. There were two streams nearby: Bayou Creek and Little Bayou Creek, which drained into the Ohio River three miles away. The Regional Gravel Aquifer was located 60 feet beneath the plant, an important drinking and water supply source for residents.

Crucial to the whole undertaking was the building of two steam plants to generate the massive amount of electricity needed to operate the cascades. The Paducah plant, said the *New York Times* in 1951, would be "the largest consumer of electricity *in the world*" [italics added].(6) The Tennessee Valley Authority was commissioned to build the Shawnee Steam Plant. Another steam plant was built in Joppa, Illinois, just across the river from Paducah, which sent a high voltage transmission line across the river. Ebasco Services of New York started the construction, which was later finished by Bechtel. (7)

ii

In 1951 Paducah seemed to come alive. Many residents worked on the construction of the plant and nearly 20,000 new workers arrived from all over the Midwest. The city became known as the Ohio River Boomtown. Land prices went up tenfold, selling for $1,000 an acre. Workers lived in trailers; people rented out spare rooms. Apartment buildings rose up; even the local brothel added a wing. A tiny town called Forrestdale was created out of 278 prefab houses which had been hauled up from Oak Ridge (initially constructed as a government "company" town). (8)   Another community was built called "Cimota," which was 'atomic' spelled backwards.

The construction of the plant began January 2, 1951 and lasted five years. The gaseous diffusion operation was gigantic, eventually covering 750 acres and consisting of 161 buildings as well as many roads and railroads. The facility cost nearly a billion dollars. Some in Congress raised questions about this astronomical rise in military spending, when we weren't at war, but Truman was intent on establishing America's nuclear superiority as the cornerstone of his foreign policy. Hans Bethe said that the scientists at Los Alamos had envisioned that, after the war, if there were *any* nuclear weapons, there would not be more than a dozen, (9) but by 1953 the US had over 300 of them and their numbers continued to rise. Eisenhower was committed to a "massive retaliation doctrine," that is, threatening any country with nuclear attack which acted in opposition to US interests. Though the American public was told that we needed to continue the arms race to "keep up" with the Soviet Union, this was not really the case. By the mid 1950s our military power exceeded the Soviets by a ratio of 40:1. As Joseph Gerson has pointed out, the purpose of our enormous nuclear arsenal was not for deterrence, but for intimidation, to establish and maintain America's global dominance. (10)   The creation of this gigantic arsenal was also, of course, enormously lucrative for the nuclear industries. Year after year, billions of tax dollars were poured their way with little AEC oversight or accountability.   (Eisenhower's warning about the Military-Industrial Complex must be taken with a grain of salt.)

In the 1950s Paducah was optimistic, seeing itself on the verge of a great future, accepting with pride its nickname "Atomic City." Like Richland, Washington near the Hanford plutonium plant (today one of the most contaminated sites on earth), Paducah was featured in *Life* magazine as one of the small

American towns enjoying the success and prosperity of the, so-called, "post-war" period. (11)

The first stage of construction was finished in September, 1952. Union Carbide, which managed the gaseous diffusion plant at Oak Ridge, assumed management of the Paducah plant as well. About 1,700 workers were hired. The huge C-331 building had 400 stages of the cascade; the later C-333 plant had 480 stages, twice the size of the plant at Oak Ridge on which it was modeled. In November, 1952 Paducah sent its first shipment -- a 2.5 ton cylinder of enriched uranium-- to Oak Ridge. The second stage of the construction involved all the other buildings of the plant, as well as two additional enrichment facilities, C-335 and C-337. (12) The workers at Paducah seemed to raise few questions about the fact that they were working at a war plant. Supporting the military was something residents of Kentucky traditionally did. Early on workers called it "the bomb plant."

The enrichment process usually began with refined uranium ore ("yellowcake") which was shipped to Paducah and refined in the conversion plant to form a black powdery substance called black oxide (uranium dioxide), to which was added hydrofluoric acid to make uranium tetrafluoride ("green salt"). This green salt was burned with fluoride to make uranium hexafluoride (UF6). The liquid form of UF6 was heated to make the gas. It was this gas which was then passed through the barriers of the cascade to separate the U-235 and U-238. The enrichment was only up to 3-5%. This "low-enriched uranium" was then condensed to a solid and packed into drums for shipping to Oak Ridge, where it was enriched up to 97% to make it usable in bombs. Later it was to be shipped to Piketon for the same purpose. During the next 50 years Paducah produced over a million tons of enriched uranium.

The jobs at Paducah were hot, high pressure, and grimy. Workers were responsible for the operation and maintenance of the plant 24 hours a day, seven days a week, overseeing and cleaning the labyrinth of pipes, pumps, motors, valves and filters, all of which required constant attention. In the summer of 1954 members of the Chemical Workers Union--at both Oak Ridge and Paducah--as a single body authorized a strike for higher wages. Union Carbide initially fought the increase, but in time a settlement was reached and wages for all Paducah workers began to climb. (13) For one thing, the plant couldn't afford to have work stoppages: it was necessary for the enrichment process to be ongoing; otherwise the gas would solidify and clog the pipes. Wages were also a way to enforce company and military loyalty. Eventually the plant became known as the best--in fact the only--good job in town. Wages and benefits for the area were high.

Uranium is far less radioactive than plutonium, but it is a health hazard when particles are inhaled; unlike plutonium it can also be fairly easily absorbed through the gastro-intestinal tract. Tests in animals have indicated uranium may damage the reproductive organs, and increase the risks of leukemia and soft tissue cancers. It is also a toxic heavy metal which can cause acute kidney damage. (14) Workers at Paducah were told that that the uranium they'd be working with was only mildly radioactive and would pose no health hazards. Until 1960 dosimeters (film badges which register radiation levels) were not required except for those working in certain high-risk areas. Dosimeter readings were done casually, if at all. Though the workers wore coveralls and gloves, most did not wear special protective clothing, nor use respirators, despite the heavy dust in the air, which they inhaled. There were no prohibitions against smoking on-site. African-Americans and women were not tested for exposure levels at all, "to simplify the data collection." (15) Accidents at the plant were common. Over 6,800 pounds of uranium hexafluoride was accidentally released into the air in November, 1960, and 3,400 pounds in 1962, only two of fifteen accidents recorded in the first ten years of the plant's operation. (16)

iii

Some of the on-site problems at Paducah due to negligence or accidents in the early years are similar to those of the other nuclear plants. The particular danger which developed at Paducah had to do with the kind of uranium used in the enrichment process. In the 1950s uranium wasn't plentiful. It took a huge amount of raw ore just to extract the tiny amount of U-235 needed, and the military was intent on building its arsenal as quickly as possible. Frenzied uranium mining was going on in Canada and the Colorado Plateau. South Africa also agreed to sell the uranium from its gold fields to Britain and the United States. All of this raw ore still wasn't enough. The Atomic Energy Commission thus made the critical decision to send to Paducah uranium which had already been used in the nuclear reactors of the plutonium production plants at Hanford and Savannah River. This uranium was "reprocessed," that is, put through a series of chemical baths and filters to separate it from the mix of nuclear waste. The scientists believed this "recycling" would be a cheap way to maintain the uranium supply and the fast pace of bomb production. The key issue, though, was that the reprocessed uranium was "tainted" with microscopic amounts of other lethal radioactive elements.

One of the contaminants was Technetium-99, a radioactive metal which is only produced when uranium is irradiated in nuclear reactors. It travels quickly though most soil and if ingested-- through drinking contaminated water or eating contaminated plants-- can concentrate as a carcinogen in the thyroid or intestinal tract. It has a half life of 210,000 years. (17) Transuranic elements in the reprocessed uranium were even more dangerous. Transuranic elements, as said before, are those with atomic weights greater than that of uranium, which is the heaviest natural element. One transuranic is neptunium; like Technetium-99 it is known to move quickly through soil and become part of underground water systems. If ingested through contaminated water or food, it is for the most part excreted within a few days. Only about .05% is not excreted, yet this tiny amount, it is believed, may lead to bone and liver cancer. Neptunium-237 has a half-life of 2.1 million years. (18) The most deadly transuranic element is Plutonium-239. It is 100,000 times more radioactive than uranium; a tiny speck inhaled in the lungs can cause cancer, and it has a half-life of 24,000 thousand years.

Officials now say that over the years 1,320 pounds of Technetium-99 was released at Paducah and over forty pounds of Neptunium-237. Only 12 ounces of Plutonium-239 was released--which doesn't sound like much-- but it was. The maximum legal limit for plutonium exposure is 0.13 micrograms; 12 ounces of plutonium could potentially endanger up to 2 ½ billion people. (19)

From 1953 to 1964, and intermittently from 1968 to 1977, Union Carbide, with AEC approval, used reprocessed uranium in the gaseous diffusion plant at Paducah. The officials knew the plant had not been designed to deal with transuranic elements, but it was faced with the option of either modifying the billion dollar plant--just finished--by requesting even more tax money for changes, or using reprocessed uranium secretly in hopes they could get away with it. From 1953-1976 more than 103,000 metric tons of reprocessed uranium was shipped to Paducah in freight cars in the form of a fine black powder, then used in the gaseous diffusion operation. (20) The workers were not told. According to a union official, the C-410 building used to process the contaminated uranium was later converted to an employee locker room and electrical repair shop. Years later shower stalls were found to be heavily contaminated with transuranic elements. (21)

Union Carbide regularly received bonuses for the "safe and efficient" operation of the plant (i.e., production totals were high). The articles in the *Washington Post* and the *Louisville Courier-Journal,* however, reveal that from the beginning the AEC and Union Carbide were aware that what they were doing was dangerous to the workers. Even though film badges in the 1950s and 1960s did not register alpha radiation-- the kind emitted by plutonium--already in 1953 there were secret company memos expressing concern that the gray powder workers were inhaling--which they called "Paducah dust"-- might be a health risk. A 1953 plant memo said: "A part of the feed material now being processed at Paducah is from Hanford reactors. It is well known that decay products will be present in major amounts...and will constitute a major radiation problem." (22) In 1960 an AEC memo to Union Carbide indicated that one government physician wanted to screen workers for exposure to transuranic elements, after an air sampling showed that concentrations of Neptunium-237 were 100 times acceptable levels. In the C-720 building, alpha-emitting radiation exceeded the plant guidelines by a factor of 1,680 for uranium, 2,121 for Neptunium-237, and 2,483 for Plutonium-239. (23) Union Carbide, however, refused to do the screenings, fearing studies might lead to "bad publicity" and unions demanding "hazard pay." Health studies were also recommended in the late 1970s and in 1985 after plutonium was found in ash coming from the plant.

The Department of Energy, however--which had replaced the Atomic Energy Commission in 1977 --never followed up. Testing for transuranic elements did not take place till 1991, forty years after the plant had opened.

Union Carbide has had a far from illustrious history when it comes to industrial safety. It was the company responsible for the catastrophic gas leak in Bhopal, India in 1984 which caused the death of at least 20,000 people, sickened or injured half a million more, and figures continue to rise. The Union- Carbide cover-up of the contamination at Paducah may have been in part to protect itself, but also in part to protect the U.S. government, which had made "secrecy" a fundamental Cold War policy. It now appears that the government was perhaps as much afraid of the American people as it was of the Soviet Union. If Americans had known the lethal danger of radiation exposure, would they have worked so eagerly at the plants? Would they have supported the expansion of the nuclear arsenal itself?

There were numerous "secret" operations going on at Paducah, as well as the enrichment operations. According to a news story in 2007, there had been a hush-hush "white room" where workers stripped precious metals such as gold and aluminum from atom bomb parts. (24) A NIRS report in 2007 expressed concern that some of the radioactive gold, later sold for commercial use, might still have had radioactive traces.(25) In another area of the plant nose cones were assembled for the Mercury Redstone missile program, and the capsule developed to send the first monkey into space. (26) Because Union Carbide knew that the uranium used at Paducah was contaminated with transuranics, a secret project was set up from April, 1958 to March, 1962 to remove neptunium from plant water. During this retrieval operation, many workers were exposed to neptunium in the air in excess of accepted levels. (27) From April, 1960 to June, 1962 a similar secret project was set up to retrieve Technetium-99 from the waste. Both projects stopped when market prices for the two metals fell. 1980 tests showed airborne radiation at the C-720 machine shop more than 2,000 times the accepted levels for both neptunium and plutonium. (28)

According to *Danger Lurks Below: The Threat to Major Water Supplies from the U.S. DOE Nuclear Weapons Plants*, seven million pounds of uranium were buried on site at Paducah between 1952 and 1985. Sixty thousand pounds were also released to local streams, and 130,000 pounds released into the air. Any uranium released into the air subsequently fell on the ground or migrated to the waters. (29) In 1994 the *New York Times* reported that from January, 1954 to September, 1955 Paducah had *intentionally* released over 650 pounds of uranium gas *a month* into the atmosphere as an experiment to test how it would be carried by the wind (using the residents of Kentucky as guinea pigs). Later controls determined that the limit of release should be less than 4 pounds *a year*. (30) Ronald Fowler, a health physicist at the plant (later a whistleblower), said that workers told him of unauthorized "purgings" of radioactive gas in the middle of the night (to get around regulations). (31)

iv

The government and the operators of the plant continued to maintain that the radiation on site was no danger to workers. The workers themselves, however, were becoming aware of cancer clusters and unusual tumors. Even plant officials began to keep a secret list of the growing number of leukemia deaths. (32) The Department of Energy did not order a health study for Paducah, though it ordered one for Oak Ridge. According to the *Washington Post*, a preliminary Oak Ridge study of 11,000 workers in 1994 found higher rates of death for all workers, and particularly high rates for lung and bone cancer, but, fearing the outcome, the DOE stopped funding the research and the study was never finished or published. (33) (This story is similar to the cancellation of funding for Dr. Thomas Mancuso's study of the health effects at Hanford, Washington in the 1970s, when the government decided it didn't want the world to know the high levels of cancer he was finding). (34) Stories of worker casualties at Paducah are listed in the 1999 *Washington Post* articles: a cascade operator who died in 1961of a rare blood/bone marrow disease at the age of 36; a cascade manager who died of leukemia in 1976 at the age of 62; a cascade operator who died in 1978 of lymphoma at the age of 54; a cascade worker who died in 1984 of a rare bone disease at the age of 64. (35)

Epidemiological studies at Paducah, like those at the other nuclear plants, have been difficult to do, but two particular stories illustrate the way in which workers themselves experienced their jobs and their illnesses. Harold Hargan began working at the plant in 1952 for $1.70 an hour. For his first assignment he was sent into a room so murky with dust and smoke he couldn't see. Workers were told, though, either to do what they were told or to leave. For most of the thirty of Hargan's 38 years at the plant, he worked in C-400 cleaning the equipment and filters. C-400 was perhaps the most contaminated building on site, because radioactivity which was washed off from the machinery concentrated in the cleaning and degreasing equipment. (C-400 was also the site of the secret operations to retrieve neptunium, technetium and gold). Some time in the mid-1950s Hargan had high radiation exposure because his boss said to him, "Don't loan anyone your urine. You're hotter than hell." Then he was simply sent back to work; there was no follow-up. In 1990 he was told he was one of six workers who had been found to have plutonium in their urine. "It surprised me. Hell, it surprised my doctor. Everyone knew there was no plutonium at Paducah." (36) Hargan is still living, but suffers from bladder cancer, mild emphysema and bronchitis. He said in 2000 that he had over $100,000 in medical bills (most insurance covered), but after the *Post* stories about the plutonium, he felt angry and betrayed. "Never did they tell us there was any danger. I think they were a bunch of liars." He was among the 10,000 former and current workers represented in a $10 billion dollar class action lawsuit filed in the fall of 1999. Later Hargan did receive federal compensation for his illnesses, but--with the upper part of his lung removed--he is still angry. (37)

Joe Harding was a press operator at Paducah who worked in the conversion facility, mixing powdered uranium with fluoride and other chemicals in "hot smoky buildings" where the gas was "so thick you could see the haze in the air when you looked at it in the ceiling light." (38) His first symptoms started a year after he began work at the plant in the early 1950s (lesions on his legs, stomach ailments and, later, fingernail-like calcium growths on his finger joints, elbows and knees). Over the years he began to keep a private record of his illnesses (his stomach was removed) and those of others at the plant. He guessed something was going on they weren't being told about, but when he spoke up about working conditions, he was called a troublemaker. He said management kept a "tight lid" on discussions of safety. Words like *radiation* were banned from conversations. (39) But his meticulous records--journals, tapes and letters--show that of the two hundred men who had been hired with him in the early years, fifty had cancer. In 1971 Union Carbide offered him full disability (because of a leg injury in a fall), but after he quit, he learned his disability claim had been denied, and he was left without pension or benefits. "They left me 50 years old with no job, and a crippled leg to get worse. No stomach, dead lungs. No way to get a job, no way to make a living." (40) He tried appealing his case, but the DOE fought him with a large contingent of lawyers. They argued that his illnesses were due to his smoking and "eating country ham." The court dismissed his claims. He said at the end of his life. "It is absolutely futile--like fighting a tiger with a toothpick." (41) He died of stomach cancer in 1980 at the age of 58. After his death his body was exhumed, and uranium was found in his bones 133 times normal levels. (42) (Harding's story was on the front page of the *Washington Post* in 1999).

v

In 1977 Paducah stopped using the recycled uranium. American nuclear bomb production had peaked in the 1960s--at approximately 34,000 weapons, enough to destroy the world many times over. After that time the production of enriched uranium at Paducah in general declined. From 1977 to the present Paducah has been the principal supplier of enriched uranium for nuclear power plants in the country. (It also currently supplies 27% of the enriched uranium used by nuclear power plants in other parts of the world). (43) In 1984 Union Carbide was replaced by Martin Marietta Energy Systems (later Lockheed Martin), part of the shifting pattern of contracts, now occurring regularly, within the inner circles of the nuclear industry. From 1984-1992 Martin Marietta operated the gaseous diffusion enrichment plants at both Paducah and Piketon--enriching the uranium to 3% at Paducah, then sending it to Piketon for enrichment up to 5%. In 1992 the Energy Policy Act established external regulations for the plant with oversight by the Occupational Safety and Health Administration (OSHA) and the Nuclear Regulatory Commission (NRC). Worker health studies began. Martin Marietta spent millions to upgrade the plant so that it could now meet health and safety standards.

In the late 1980s, however, evidence emerged that radioactive contamination had already spread outside the plant. In 1988 Plutonium-239 and Neptunium-237 were both found in offsite wells nine miles away from the plant. Though plant officials continued publicly to deny they had found evidence of plutonium in the plant and surrounding areas, private maps and documents--acquired by the *Washington Post* through the Freedom of Information Act--show that officials had been looking for plutonium for years and had found it "nearly everywhere they looked." (44) In the 1990s investigators discovered that dumping both radioactive and chemical wastes had been casual, sometimes illegal, for years. Sometimes workers dumped contaminated waste water into a stretch of the North-South Diversion Ditch, which ran into the Little Bayou Creek, which eventually flows into the Ohio River. Sometimes radioactive and hazardous waste chemicals were dumped together (against regulation); sometimes radioactive and/or hazardous wastes were dumped at sanitary landfills (supposedly only for garbage). (45) Thousands of gallons of contaminated materials leaked from large pits on site. Some of the hazardous chemical wastes were PCB and dioxin, both carcinogens, and TCE (trichloroethylene), a toxic carcinogenic chemical which had been used extensively in cleaning the pipes of the cascades.

In the 1990s the EPA found two dozen unlicensed radioactive debris piles. In February, 2000, 16,000 tons of "special" nuclear weapons hardware was discovered buried on site in a classified underground storage depot. (46) In July, 2000 a radioactive black ooze was found a quarter mile from the plant with uranium and technetium levels hundreds of times above normal. (47)

In May, 1994 Paducah had officially been put on the National Priorities List and made eligible for Superfund status. Bechtel-Jacobs, another common player in the nuclear conglomerate, had been given the contract to begin remediation work at all three of the gaseous diffusion plants at Oak Ridge, Paducah and Piketon, even though all were still operating.

One of the greatest concerns at Paducah has been the contaminated aquifer beneath the C-400 building at the center of the site. It was in C-400 that the degreaser TCE had been used for cleaning the pipes; sometimes, workers said, TCE waste had even been poured directly down the drains. According to the DOE, 180,000 gallons of TCE may be present in the aquifer at concentrations far exceeding regulatory levels. (48) The aquifer has also become severely contaminated with Technetium-99, which had been in the radioactive material clinging to the pipes. Studies in the late 1990s showed that three plumes of water contaminated with TCE and Technetium-99 were spreading northward from the plant at a rate of a foot a day, and had already extended over two miles beyond the limits of the plant. (49) In April, 2000 David Michaels, the DOE assistant secretary for the environment, said that he believed that one of the plumes had already reached the Ohio River. (50)

Trying to deal with contaminated water is one of the greatest difficulties facing all the nuclear plants. The technology of "clean-up" of nuclear waste is still in its infancy; there is no way to know how effective the cleanup measures being used at the present time will be. In late 1980s the engineers tried pumping to the surface one billion gallons of contaminated water from the aquifer beneath the C-400 plant, but this treatment method didn't work because the contamination from C-400 was still going on. A new method recently proposed will involve burying electrodes in the ground beneath the building to evaporate the TCE. The vapor will then be pumped to the surface and trapped in carbon filters. In a test run, this method proved effective, but it is not known if it will work on a large scale. (51) According to *Danger Lurks Below*, the TCE seems to be settling in pools at the bottom of the aquifer, making it hard to remove. (52) Another problem with this vapor method is that the Technetium-99, which is radioactive, *cannot* be removed by the electrodes. Brian Smith, director of the Kentucky Division of Waste Management, said, "We'll deal with that as the project moves along." (53) A number of other methods for cleaning the aquifer have been tried, but so far none has been successful. USEC, the corporation which at the present time manages the gaseous diffusion operation, plans to decontaminate some of the uranium with technetium traces, but it is not involved in the cleanup of the water. (54)

In the summer of 2005 the DOE set aside $15 million in order to buy out the land of the 120 families whose homes and businesses are on top of the contaminated plume. (For years the DOE has been paying $70,000-$100,000 a year for the families to get free city water since they can't use their wells). (55) In the spring of 2007, however, the DOE said that it had "no plans" to buy the land, so residents remain unclear as to what their futures will be. (56)

Already there is fear that the contaminated water moving off site has led to radiation and toxic chemicals being absorbed by plants and animals. Even though plutonium is not usually assimilated in the gastro-intestinal tract of human beings, it decays into another isotope called americium, which is easily absorbed by plants and then the animals which eat those plants. (57) In 1994 a tiny amount of plutonium was found in a deer killed offsite. (58) According to an article in the *Louisville Courier-Journal*, already there is considerable evidence that nearby wildlife have been contaminated by hazardous chemicals as well. Fish found in Big Bayou Creek show increasing levels of toxic metals; PCB has been found from traces to significant levels in fish, hawks, mice, rats, and mink. (59)

Mrs. Wilma Kelly, whose home borders the plant and has a drainage ditch from the plant in the front of her house, said that a few years ago the apple trees in her front yard suddenly became warped and died. ("They just shrunk up, deformed.") She was concerned about all the apples which her family ate, but also angry that "the workers can't prove nothing." (60) Traces of neptunium had been found in some of the apples near the plant. (61) Scientists from Texas Tech found high radioactive levels in raccoons (a significant fact because raccoons eat everything, showing contamination is in the food chain). (62) Technetium-99 has been found in vegetables grown near the plant (turnips, beets, lettuce, squash). Biologists have also discovered insects in the area with deformed eyes. Eyes from the larvae of midges sometimes were found to be not properly defined, fused together, or missing. In some cases eyes were forming in the wrong places. (63) Ecologists today have two primary fears about the contamination showing up in plants and wildlife in Paducah: one, that radiation and toxins will be passed on to human beings--a lot of hunting still goes on in the wildlife refuge surrounding the plant-- and two, that the genetic malformations will affect the ability of wildlife itself to stay alert, reproduce and survive. (64)

vi

A month after the *Washington Post* stories in August, 1999, Bill Richardson, then the DOE secretary under Clinton, made a special trip to Paducah and publicly apologized to the workers and residents for government deception and neglect. Richardson told the workers: "On behalf of the government I'm here to say I'm sorry. The men and women who have worked in this facility helped the United States in the Cold War and now help us keep the peace." (65) Though the role of nuclear weapons as "peacekeepers" is questionable, given the many global conflicts the last fifty years and continuing fears and tensions, Richardson was trying to reach out to the men and women contaminated at the plant and indirectly acknowledge past government mistakes. For at least 10 years, studies had shown the risks to nuclear workers, but the federal government had ignored these studies. (66) Richardson also promised the workers financial compensation. In 2000 the Energy Employee Occupational Illness Compensation Program Act was passed by Congress guaranteeing $150,000 and free health monitoring for life to workers who may have been contaminated by contact with radioactive materials at the nuclear weapons plants. A "Special Cohort" category was established for those workers at the three enrichment plants--Oak Ridge, Paducah and Piketon-- acknowledging that the dangers of their exposure were high--perhaps also because they had been lied to and unprotected against the transuranic elements. In 2004, due to many petitions by former workers, the DOE also agreed to compensate workers made ill through chemical exposures at these plants, as well as radiation.

As of summer, 2005 only 18% of the 8,416 Paducah workers who filed for the nuclear compensation had received the settlement. The requirements to receive the compensation were for employees to have worked at the plant for at lease 250 days and contracted silicosis, beryllium disease or one of 22 specified cancers. Though the number of successful claims does not seem large (certainly to the former workers it doesn't), workers at Oak Ridge, Piketon and Paducah have had a higher number of claims granted than workers at other nuclear plants because of their Special Cohort Status. (67) At all the other plants, including Mound and Fernald, sick workers have had to go through an elaborate individual dose-reconstruction process to determine if exposure levels could have contributed to their illnesses, and far fewer of their claims have been recognized. (Workers at both Mound and Fernald are now trying to get the rules changed so that they can be designated as having Special Cohort status as well.)

In Paducah today there is a Sick Workers Office and a mobile unit which regularly does lung x-rays throughout the city. In the summer of 2005 the workers who had filed claims and been granted compensation based on chemical exposures still had not received their checks. To workers such as Raleigh Struble, suffering from lead poisoning and unable to walk, the delays were frustrating. (68) Cancer of residents living near the plant also seems to be becoming more common. According to Paducah activist Ron Lamb, there is one street near the plant which is considered by local residents a "hot spot," because 40-50 people have died of cancer there. (69)

In 1992 the United States Enrichment Corporation (USEC) took over from Martin Marietta and assumed management of both Paducah and Piketon. (The story of USEC will be told in the next chapter). In 2002 USEC announced it was going to close the Piketon plant. With the Oak Ridge enrichment plant being "decontaminated and decommissioned," Paducah became the country's sole producer of enriched uranium. In July, 2004, however, USEC shifted direction again, saying that it was going to build a new centrifuge enrichment plant at Piketon and permanently close Paducah in 2010. One of the reasons USEC gave for closing Paducah was the still huge electricity costs of operating the gaseous diffusion operation ($25.4 million *a month,* $305 million a year--60% of production costs)--not to mention all the air pollution from the electrical generators. (70) The centrifuge method, USEC said, would be better because it would take far less electricity, but it would still, of course, generate more radioactive waste.

Another company has been hired --Uranium Disposition Services-- to deal with the 39,000 cylinders of depleted uranium on site. The enrichment process the last 40 years to extract the tiny amount of fissionable U-235 for bombs and power plants created enormous quantities of U-238. The operators of the plant maintain that the depleted uranium is safe in the cylinders onsite, and has always been safe, yet nearly all scientists disagree with them. One of the dangers is that the depleted uranium hexafluoride is potentially explosive until it can be converted to a more stable form. Uranium hexafluoride explosions did occur in 1978 at the Allied Chemical plant in Metropolis, Illinois, across the river from Paducah, and at the Kerr-McGee Sequoyah plant in Gore, Oklahoma in 1986, where one person died and many were injured. (71)

Uranium Disposition Services proposes to convert the uranium hexafluoride to a stable form and then extract hydrofluoric acid for commercial sale. Because of the plutonium-contamination, however, the sale of the acid may not be viable. Even if it is, certain other questions have been raised about the conversion process. A recent discovery of the toxic chemical phosgene in some of the depleted uranium barrels has indicated there may be some chemical problems with the planned conversion. (72) Dr. Arjun Makhijani, one of the world's leading experts on nuclear waste, recently wrote in favor of Uranium Disposition Services doing "something" about the dangerous cylinders, but said its method to convert the depleted uranium into a form of oxide could ultimately lead to leachate in the ground. (He feels the depleted uranium should be converted into ceramic pellets which could be more safely stored for the billions of years the DU will remain radioactive). (73) In spring, 2007 USEC proposed that the DOE "transfer"—that is, give to them—the 55 million pounds of depleted uranium to enrich further to use as feed material at Paducah, but this seems more of a ploy in response to USEC's current financial problems than anything else, since neither the technology nor the economics of this proposal is certain. (74)

At the end of 2005, Bechtel Jacobs withdrew from the cleanup operations, and after a complex bidding war, a new three-year contract was given to Paducah Remediation Services, a joint venture of Shaw Environmental and Portage Environmental (the same companies given the contract to remediate the OU-1 site at Mound). PRS will be responsible for continuing the work begun by Bechtel: groundwater and soil cleanup, removing old waste, cleaning up and removing old contaminated buildings, and operating waste storage buildings. (75) PRS reduced by 150 the staff used by Bechtel-Jacobs. (76) Much of the waste from Paducah is being sent for storage to the Nevada Test Site.

In Paducah, as in most of the other nuclear sites, a Citizens Advisory Board (CAB) was formed in the 1990s, supposedly to allow the community some say in the cleanup and future use of the site. According to the former CAB chair Mark Donham, for a time an environmentalist majority on the board in Paducah was able to stop the DOE from reducing the cleanup levels. The DOE promised to notify the board before an official cleanup agreement with the state was reached, but did not. Members of the CAB read about the agreement one morning in the *Paducah Sun* and seven resigned in protest, feeling that "community participation" in the decision-making process had been a sham. (77)

vii

Today the residents of Paducah are living as best they can with the realities of their nuclear history. About 1,700 still work at the plant; it continues to be the largest private employer in western Kentucky. Bobbie Ann Mason has written a novel sympathetic to current plant workers (*Atomic Romance*). Many are still worried about pensions, health insurance, and the future shutdown. Residents of Paducah are also worried about whether the federal government will continue to pay for the cleanup which still needs to be done, and for the monitoring of people and the ecosystem long into the future. Federal cleanup funds for Paducah are shrinking at the rate of 15% a year ($190 million in 2004, $174 million in 2005, and $159 million in 2006). (79) As a way to make money for cleanup operations, Rep. Edward Whitfield (R-KY) proposed in June, 2006 to rescind a Clinton administration policy which banned the recycling of metals contaminated with plutonium, so that Paducah could begin selling the 9,700 tons of contaminated nickel to India and China, where demand is high. (79) A few refineries have said this nickel could be processed to remove all radioactive traces (80), but the NIRS report, *Out of Control--On Purpose,* is extremely skeptical of this view. (81) The local business community headed by PACRO (the Paducah Area Community Reuse Organization) strongly favors lifting the nickel ban.

In late 2006 the people of Paducah learned that the site could be the location of a *new* nuclear operation, its own reprocessing plant, which would process spent fuel rods from nuclear reactors to make usable uranium and plutonium. A local business coalition received a federal grant of $664,600 to study the feasibility of locating a reprocessing plant near the edge of the gaseous diffusion site. (Piketon received a similar study grant.) (82) Reprocessing is one of the key ideas of George Bush's Global Nuclear Energy Partnership (GNEP), designed to promote the use (and lucrative sale) of nuclear power plants throughout the world, and (it is feared) also make plutonium available again for weapons. Reprocessing is dangerous and expensive, and would involve the transport of the highly radioactive fuel rods to Kentucky from throughout the country and perhaps the world. Though one can sympathize with the fear of many Paducah residents about the jobs which will be lost when the gaseous diffusion plant closes, one still can't help but wonder what they are thinking. It was the use of reprocessed uranium which caused all the transuranic contamination of the site in the first place. The only commercial reprocessing plant in the United States, in West Valley, New York, was shut down in the 1970s after only a few years of operation due to major technological problems, and left so much highly radioactive waste that, even after a $5.2 billion "cleanup," the groundwater and the Great Lakes watershed are still endangered. (83)   Reprocessing plants in Europe have also been plagued by accidents. The worst nuclear disaster in history was the 1957 explosion of a waste tank at the Chelyabinsk reprocessing plant in southern Russia, which released an enormous amount of plutonium into the air and permanently contaminated 6,000 square miles. Windscale, in Sellafield, England, is now shut down due to problems. The reprocessing plants in England and France also created huge volumes of liquid waste which was discharged into the sea--which has angered other European countries. (84)

It doesn't seem likely that Paducah will be chosen as the location of a new reprocessing plant, particularly because it is close to the New Madrid earthquake fault. (The 6.8 earthquake in the summer of 2007 which caused radioactive releases from the Kashiwazaki-Kariwa plant in Japan rattled the world nuclear community a great deal). (85) Paducah mayor Bill Paxton, however, is still lobbying hard for the plant.   The governor of Kentucky contributed $228,721 for the preliminary study. (86). Unions are strongly behind the idea, and many people are talking about Paducah again becoming a "boom town." The Paducah task force (which includes several former USEC officials) submitted its site analysis to the DOE in May, 2007, but it will not be known for another year whether the site is chosen. (87) Amid all these plans for the future, federal funding for the cleanup and compensation for ailing workers from the past continues to decline.

Notes: Paducah

1. Mason, Bobbie Ann, "Fallout: Paducah's Secret Nuclear Disaster," *The New Yorker,* January 10, 2000, 30.

2. Carroll, James R. and James Malone, "Toxins Altering Life in Fragile Eco-system," *Louisville Courier-Journal,* June 26, 2000.

3. Rhodes, Richard, *The Making of the Atomic Bomb* (New York: Simon and Schuster, 1986), 500.

4. Radioactive Waste Management Associates. *Danger Lurks Below: The Threat to Major Water Supplies from the U.S. DOE Nuclear Weapons Plants.* (Washington, D.C.: Alliance for Nuclear Accountability, 2004), xi. (www.ananuclear.org)

5. Makhijani, Arjun, Howard Hu and Katherine Yih, eds. *Nuclear Wastelands. A Global Guide to Nuclear Weapons Production and Its Health and Environmental Effects* (Cambridge, Mass.: MIT Press, 1995), 205-206.

6. Swift, Thomas P. "Power Plant to Aid A.E.C. Project to Become $100,000,000 Utility," *New York Times,* July 22, 1951, 93.

7. "Bechtel Will Build Joppa Power Plant," *New York Times,* August 5, 1953, 38.

8. Malone, James, "'Almost Overnight, Paducah Became the Promised Land,'" *Louisville Courier-Journal,* June 25, 2000.

9. Bethe, Hans, *The Road From Los Alamos* (New York: Simon and Schuster, 1991), 53.

10. Gerson, Joseph. *Empire and the Bomb: How the US Uses Nuclear Weapons to Dominate the World* (Ann Arbor: Pluto Press, 2007), 180.

11. Malone, "'Almost Overnight.'"

12. "Weapons of Mass Destruction: Paducah Gaseous Diffusion Plant," Global-Security.Org (www.globalsecurity.org/wmd/facilities/paducah.htm)

13. Abel, Elie, "Pay Pact is Likely at Atomic Plants," *New York Times,* July 26,1954, 18.

14. "Fact Sheet: Fissile Materials Health & Environmental Dangers." Institute for Energy and Environmental Research. (www.ieer.org/fctsheet/fm_hlth.html)

15. Malone, James, "U.S. Says Radiation Caused Illnesses," *Louisville Courier-Journal,* January 25, 2000.

16. "History Reveals Ignorance, Concealment, Peril," *Louisville Courier-Journal,* July 27, 2000.

17. "EPA Facts about Technetium-99." U.S. Environmental Protection Agency, July 2002. (http://www.epa.gov/superfund/resources/radiation/PDF/technetium.pdf)

18. "Neptunium: Human Health Fact Sheet," Argonne National Laboratory, July, 2002. (www.ead.anl.gov/pub/doc/neptunium.pdf)

19. Mason, "Fallout" p. 33.

20. Warrick, Joby, "In Harm's Way, And in the Dark: Workers Exposed to Plutonium at U.S. Plant," *Washington Post,* August 8, 1999, A1.

21. Owens, Leon, "Testimony at the Committee on Senate Energy and Natural Resources." Washington, D.D. November 21, 2003. (www.energy.senate.gov/hearings/testimony.cfm?id=1001&wit_id=2888-35k-supplemental result)

22. Malone, James, "Former Worker Now Believes Paycheck Came with a Price," *Louisville Courier-Journal,* June 25, 2000.

23. Owens.

24. Walker, Joe, "Behind Closed Doors, Almost 50 Years Ago, Paducah Workers Built a Monkey's Space Capsule," *Paducah Sun,* January 28, 2007.

25. D'Arrigo and Mary Olson. *Out of Control--On Purpose: DOE's Dispersal of Radioactive Waste into Landfills and Consumer Products* (Takoma Park: IEER, 2007), 23.

26. Walker, "Behind Closed Doors."

27. Malone, James, "Workers Weren't Told About Animal Experiments," *Louisville Courier-Journal,* June 25, 2000.

28. Malone, "Former Worker."

29. Radioactive Waste Management 147.

30. "Radioactive Gas Experiments Come to Light," *New York Times,* August 6, 1994, 9.

31. Auster, Bruce B. "Indecent Exposures: Why Radioactive Contamination Bedevils a Kentucky Town," *US News & World Report,* 127 *(*August 30, 1999) 35.

32. Malone, James and James R. Carroll, "U.S. Ignored Leukemia Concerns," *Louisville Courier-Journal,* September 5, 1999, 1A.

33. Warrick, Joby, "Paducah's Silent Witness," *Washington Post,* August 22, 1999, A1.

34. Gould, Jay and Benjamin A. Goldman, *Deadly Deceit: Low Level Radiation, High-Level Coverup* (New York: Four Walls Eight Windows, 1990) 88.

35. Warrick, Joby, "Plant Hid Risks from Workers," *Washington Post,* December 23, 1999, A1.

36. Malone, "Former Worker."

37. Walker, Joe, "Frustration Grows as Sick Workers Wait for Benefits," *Paducah Sun,* August 26, 2005.

38. Wasserman, Harvey and Norman Solomon, with Robert Alvarez and Eleanor Walters, *Killing Our Own: The Disaster of America's Experience with Atomic Radiation* (New York; Delacorte Press, 1982), 157.

39. Wasserman 157.

40. Warrick, Joby, "A Deathly Postscript Comes Back to Life," *Washington Post,* August 11, 1999, A1.

41. Warrick, "Deathly Postscript."

42. Warrick, "Paducah's Silent Witness."

43. "Truck Carrying Radioactive Material Involved in Minor Crash," *Associated Press State and Local Wire Service,* January 4, 2007.

44. Warrick, Joby, "Maps Reveal Scattering of Kentucky Plutonium," *Washington Post,* October 1, 2000, A1.

45. Malone, James and James R. Carroll, "Kentucky Has Gone Easy on Uranium Plant," *Louisville Courier-Journal,* June 27, 2000. See also D'Arrigo and Olson, *Out of Control--on Purpose,* p.38.

46. "Nukes Buried in Kentucky," *Cincinnati Post,* February 12, 2000, 4A.

47. Warrick, Joby and Joe Stephens. "Radioactive Ooze Found in Paducah," *Washington Post,* August 29, 1999.

48. Walker, Joe, "Water Cleanup Good, but Not Foolproof at Paducah Gaseous Diffusion Plant," *Paducah Sun,* August 10, 2005.

49. Warrick, Joby, "Safety Measures Ordered at Kentucky Uranium Plant," *Washington Post,* September 15, 1999, A2.

50. Carroll, James R., "Uranium Cleanup Cost Likely to Grow Sharply, Report Says." *Louisville Courier-Journal,* April 1, 2000, 1A.

51. Walker, "Water Cleanup."

52. Radioactive Waste Management 150.

53. Walker, "Water Cleanup."

54. Knapik, Michael, "USEC to Finish Cleanup of Uranium by October 2008, GAO Report Says," *Nucleonics Week,* 47 (July 6, 2006), 19.

55. "Congress May Require DOE to Study Buyout of Contaminated Paducah Land," *Waste and Hazardous Substances* 10 (July 11, 2005).

56. Walker, Joe, "DOE Not Seeking Landowner Buyout," *Paducah Sun,* March 15, 2007.

57. "Americium: Human Health Fact Sheet." Argonne National Laboratory, EVS. April, 2005.

58. "History Reveals Ignorance."

59. Carroll and Malone, "Toxins Altering Life."

60. Stephens, Joe, "A New Sense of Fear Settles on Paducah," *Washington Post,* August 21, 1999, A1.

61. Carroll and Malone, "Toxins Altering,"

62. Carroll, James R. "Raccoons Show Scientists Contaminants Are Accumulating," *Louisville Courier-Journal,* June 26, 2000.

63. Carroll and Malone, "Toxins Altering."

64. Carroll, "Raccoons Show."

65. Warrick, Joby, "Radiation Risks Long Concealed," *Washington Post,* September 21, 1999, A1.

66. Alvarez, Robert, "Risks to Uranium Process Workers." Institute for Policy Studies.
(www.ips-dc.org/projects/nuclear/index.htm)

67. Rogers, Keith, "Cold War Compensation: Analysis Finds Disparity," *Las Vegas Review-Journal,* August 7, 2005.

68. Walker, "Frustration Grows."

69. Lamb, Ron, "Uranium in the Nuclear Weapons Complex Panel: Paducah." Alliance for Nuclear Accountability Meeting, Cincinnati, Ohio, October 22, 2005.

70. Walker, Joe, "USEC, Needing to Cut Costs, Cuts 50 Salaried Jobs," *Paducah Sun,* August 17, 2005.

71. Diamond, Stuart. "Uranium Plant Where Man Died Was Cited for Leaks of Pollution," *New York Times,* January 13, 1986.

72. "Committee Approves Study of Toxic Gas at Paducah Plant," *Associated Press State & Local Wire,* November 9, 2005. For the current controversy about this report, see Brett Barrouquere, "Report: Study of Toxic Gas at Paducah's Nuclear Plant Flawed," *Associated Press,* June 5, 2007.

73. Walker, Joe, "Author Raises Safety Question over Rush to Build Nuclear Fuel Plants," *Paducah Sun,* February 27, 2005.

74. Walker, Joe, "The Value of Spent Uranium: USEC Lobbies for Transfer of Paducah Cylinders' Content amid Rising Power Costs of Gaseous Diffusion," *Paducah Sun,* April 1, 2007.

75. "U. S. Department of Energy Awards Paducah Remediation Contract: Paducah Remediation Service, LLC Wins $191 Million Small Business Contract Competition." Energy Department Documents and Publications, December 27, 2005.

76. Walker, Joe , "DOE Cleanup to Employ 400 at Job's Start," *Paducah Sun,* April 21, 2006.

77. Donham, Mark, "Uranium in the Nuclear Weapons Complex Panel: Paducah." Alliance for Nuclear Accountability Meeting, Cincinnati, Ohio, October 22, 2005.

78. Lamb.

79. Hansen, Brian, "At Hearing, DOE Urged to Lift Ban on Recycling of Contaminated Metal," *Inside Energy,* January 23, 2006, 7.

80. Walker, Joe, "Companies Tour Nuclear Plant in Hopes of Buying Scrap Nickel: The Price of the Metal has risen to $50,000 a ton based on Demand from China and India, " *Paducah Sun,* April 4, 2007.

81. D'Arrigo and Olson 17.

82. "DOE Awards Over $10 Million for GNEP Siting Studies," *World Nuclear News,* January 31, 2007.

83. "Just Say No to the Radioactive Waste Reprocessing Relapse," Nuclear Information and Resource Service Alert, May 24, 2005. (www.nirs.org/alerts/05-24-2005/2)

84. Makhijani, Arjun, "International Experience with Reprocessing and Related Technologies," Institute for Environment Energy and Research Fact Sheet, January 25, 2006. (www.ieer.org/fctsheet/repro-intl.html)

85. "Governor Fletcher Announces State Funding for Paducah Energy Project," *US States News,* February 2, 2007.

86. "Experts to Visit Japanese Plant," *BBC News,* August 5, 2007.

87. "Study: Potential Earthquake Biggest Obstacle for Paducah Plant," *Associated Press State & Local Wire,* May 6, 2007.

Future Of Uncertainty: Portsmouth Gaseous Diffusion Plant, Piketon, Ohio

Southeastern Ohio is on the edge of the Appalachian mountains, an area of hills, forests, rivers and small lakes. Thousands of years ago Adena-Hopewell mound builders lived in the region, as they did near Miamisburg. There is a Mound Cemetery near Piketon, several mound works in nearby Waverly, and archeological sites throughout the region. A recent geological study of the famous Serpent Mound in nearby Adams County has discovered high levels of iridium in the rocks beneath the site. Some scientists believe that a meteor once crashed into the earth near the site, and that the serpent mound was perhaps built in awed response to the event. One rather eerie comment by the scientists is that microscopic fractures in quartz crystals found at the site resemble patterns of rocks at the Nuclear Test Site in Nevada. (1)

Before the coming of European-Americans, the area of southeastern Ohio was inhabited by Shawnee and Wyandotte Indians. The entire history of the region--from Shawnee villages to present day businesses--is displayed today on a large vivid mural by Robert Dafford, 20 feet high and thousands of feet long, which is on the flood wall in Portsmouth, Ohio. (Dafford is doing a similar mural for the flood wall at Paducah.) One of the panels of the mural shows the uranium enrichment plant, a major employer of the area. Like the other nuclear locations, however, Piketon has had severe problems with health and safety issues, and is now having to deal with contamination both on and off site. Unlike Mound, Paducah, Fernald, Maxey Flats and Jefferson Proving Ground--which are all now closed or being closed--a private company is building a pilot for a new centrifuge enrichment plant at Piketon. A group of Ohio investors has also received federal funds to study the feasibility of locating either a nuclear reprocessing plant or a radioactive waste disposal site at Piketon, proposals which have generated great local controversy. Piketon may be facing hazards from exposure and contamination for a long time to come.

European-Americans first moved into the region in the late 1700s, not long after the defeat of the Indians at the Battle of Fallen Timbers and the subsequent illegal seizure of Indian land. Pike County was founded in 1815. An early Ohio governor from Piketon negotiated for part of the Ohio Erie Canal to go through the area (near land he himself owned). The first millionaire of Pike County, James Emmitt, built canal boats, distilleries, mills and other enterprises. After the Civil War and the decline of river commerce, most people in the area worked on small farms, in lumber mills or scattered factories. (2) In the twentieth century southeastern Ohio suffered considerable economic hardship. The poet James Wright, from Martin's Ferry, often wrote about the loneliness and desolation of modern Ohio River towns.

Scientists in the Manhattan Project had discovered that, if uranium were enriched to a low level first, then to a higher level, the yield would be greater. Paducah was built to do the first stage of enrichment (3-5%); a second plant would then enrich it up to 97% for bombs. Many states lobbied to get the second plant, but the final choice seems to have been between Cincinnati and Piketon. As already stated, Cincinnati was in the process of building the Fernald plant to manufacture uranium ingots. Though some city leaders--and many union leaders--wanted the enrichment plant too, a number (including the Chamber of Commerce) did not. Some said Cincinnati didn't have the labor force to undertake a second massive federal building project, and they didn't like the idea of more "outsiders" coming in. (3) The Ohio Lieutenant Governor at the time was George D. Nye of Pike County. Nye aggressively promoted Piketon as the site for the enrichment plant, despite the objections of local naturalists and archeologists. (4) The site was suitable, he said, because of its nearness to the cheap coal of West Virginia and Kentucky. Another factor in the final selection of Piketon was its location on the Scioto River. In 1952 a Columbus paper reported that "the Ohio Water Pollution Control Board--which won't countenance dumping of radioactive or other industrial waste into the Scioto River --will require the plant to obtain a discharge permit, even though it is a Federal project." (5) What happened to the state's "not countenancing" radioactive discharge into the Scioto isn't clear, for during the next thirty-six years all surface water from the plant eventually drained into the Scioto and then into the Ohio. According to *Danger Lurks Below,* the onsite water was heavily contaminated by uranium as well as other radionuclides and toxic chemicals. (6)

At the time the Portsmouth Gaseous Diffusion Plant was built, Pike was the third smallest county in Ohio: not many jobs, no crime, few health problems. (7) In 1952 the government acquired 3,708 acres of relatively flat land between Piketon and Wakefield, one mile east of the Scioto River, about 15 miles north of the city of Portsmouth on the Ohio River. Two new power plants were built to generate the enormous electricity needed for the cascades: one at Kyger Creek in Cheshire, Ohio, another at Clifty Creek in Madison, Indiana. The plant required at peak over 1.8 million kilowatts. (8) By the mid- 1960s, in fact, the electrical generators for the three gaseous diffusion plants at Oak Ridge, Paducah, and Piketon consumed 6% of the electrical output of *the whole country--*a never-discussed factor in America's "energy crisis. " (9) To produce this electricity, the utility plants used millions of tons of coal a year, generating high levels of toxic sulfur dioxide emissions which spread for hundreds of miles.

The immediate community response to the coming of the plant to Piketon, though, was like that of Paducah, one of euphoria because of the job opportunities. Residents still refer to the time as The Boom. The owner of the only hotel in town said the value of her property doubled within three hours after the official announcement. The Democratic speaker of the Kentucky House of Representatives promised to build a 200-unit trailer court in Piketon, similar to one he had already built near the plant in Paducah. (10) Construction on the plant-- tentatively called the "Portsmouth Project"--began. It was completed six months ahead of schedule in March, 1956, at a final cost of $750 million. More than 1,200 acres of forest had been cleared, and more than 4.5 million cubic yards of earth removed in a massive flattening of the once beautiful, lush green landscape. In constructing the main entrance ramp to the plant, the builders damaged part of an ancient alembic earthwork, which local preservationists today are trying to restore. (11) Over a hundred large square buildings at the plant covered 640 acres.(12) The first manager, Goodyear Atomic Corporation, was a subsidiary of Goodyear Tire and Rubber of Akron. Union Carbide, which managed Paducah, was hired to give "technical assistance" to the Goodyear management. (13)

ii

For the next fifteen years the Piketon plant operated in southeastern Ohio without much attention from the outside world, further enriching the uranium it received from Paducah and Oak Ridge. The basic gaseous diffusion method was the same at all three plants: uranium hexafluoride gas was pumped through the porous nickel barriers of the cascade, separating the lighter U-235 from the heavier U-238. The cascade at Piketon was housed in three huge warehouse-like structures: X333, X330 and X326. Each building had two floors and over fifty *acres* of floor space. The enrichment took place on the second floor; the control and auxiliary systems were on the first. (14) The U-235, enriched to 97%, was shipped in solid form from Piketon in 10-liter steel bottles to fabrication plants which then converted it into uranium oxide or uranium metal. This highly enriched uranium was used not only for bombs, but also for fuel for submarines which were propelled by nuclear reactors. The vast quantity of U-238 (depleted uranium) which was created by the enrichment process at Piketon was stored in large metal canisters, as it was at Paducah. Workers called the site the A-Plant. Like the workers at Paducah, they undertook the grimy difficult work without asking many questions about what they were doing or why. They were told the uranium they were processing would not pose any serious health dangers, that it was "safe enough to eat" (a phrase often heard at Paducah and Fernald as well).

The facility, however, had many hidden dangers in the early years, some of which were described in a series of detailed articles by Tom Beyerlein and Lynn Hulsey in the *Dayton Daily News* in November, 2006. A DOE investigation in 2000 revealed over 400 documented accidental releases of uranium gas or toxic fluorine gas during the thirty-six years of the plant's operation; there were probably many more which were undocumented. Wastes and chemical contaminants were improperly dumped in unlined ponds, landfills and ditches. (15) In addition, from the 1950s to the 1970s, two oil-based incinerators burned uranium-contaminated waste which routinely produced heavy black smoke. Incineration does not destroy radioactivity, but simply disperses radionuclides into the air. The oil-based incinerators were replaced in 1971 by a dual-chamber incinerator, which workers called "the Radicator."(16) When it was closed in 1986 soil around the incinerator was discovered to be radioactive at least 12 feet deep. (17) Brian Blair of the Ohio EPA, who took part in the state's first inspection of the site in 1986, said, "[Plants] were not managed even according to the best technology available at that time. That's why we have many of the contaminants out there." (18)

In addition, as at Paducah, the workers at Piketon were not told that some of the uranium was "reprocessed," that is, contaminated with plutonium and other transuranic elements. How much plutonium was in the enriched material shipped up from Paducah isn't known, but from 1957 to 1978 Piketon had had its own oxide conversion facility: the E area of building X705. Because records don't exist, we don't know how much contaminated uranium was processed there, or how much plutonium and other transuranic elements workers were exposed to. (19) When the E area was sealed and permanently closed in 1978, however, it was considered "highly radioactively contaminated." (20) In 1977 plant operators found low levels of plutonium and neptunium in sediment samples from Little and Big Beaver Creek. (21) In 1962 Goodyear had issued a *Health Physics Philosophy as a Guide for Housekeeping Problems in the Process Area* ("housekeeping" was a euphemism for radiation monitoring). Managers had been told then to keep the monitoring information to themselves. "We don't expect or desire that the philosophy will be openly discussed with bargaining unit employees." (22) Dangers were concealed so that workers would not demand hazard pay, compensation for illnesses, or perhaps refuse to work at all.

The main contaminant in the X705 building was Technetium-99, which adhered to the pipes and equipment of the cascades. Workers described it as a dark gooey sludge which looked like black tobacco juice. (23) When technetium compounds reacted with moist air, an acid was formed which diffused as gas. Workers were sometimes exposed to technetium when equipment was opened for repairs, upgrades or replacement. In 1976 when Larry Knapp, a crane operator, was pulling a giant uranium compressor from its moorings, a great cloud of yellow gas suddenly enveloped him. He put on his respirator and managed to move the crane slowly to an exit. Knapp survived the accident, but for the next 30 years he suffered skin lesions and had to have over a hundred skin grafts, for which he has received neither federal nor worker's compensation. (24) In 1979 when seals were being removed from a converter, smoke began to rise from X705. Large red and orange clouds were soon swirling from the building and being carried off into other areas by strong drafts. Technetium levels were monitored and found to be 5.7 times allowable levels. (25) One employee said six workers were severely exposed then. (26) Technetium could also have been released over the years through ventilation systems, doors and windows. In fact, the reason given by the DOE for stopping the conversion operation in the E area in 1978 was that the "facility could not meet current standards for containment as manifested in high levels of airborne contamination." (27)

Most of the technetium, however, was released as liquid effluent generated by the cleaning of the pipes. In 1975, due to an accident, technetium was found in the east draining ditch exceeding the Ohio radiation limit more than 300,000 times. (28) Even though the plant later tried to correct the problem of technetium in the water by building an ion-exchange facility, the ion exchange resins were still "hot" and simply put in 55-gallon drums in the outdoor hot yard. (29) According to a later report, these resins were put in unlined landfills, along with spent filter material from the cascades and other contaminated solid matter, and leaked into the groundwater again. (30) The presence of the technetium in the ground water, as at Paducah, is a danger to the ecosystem. Residents already fear radioactive contamination may have been absorbed by plants and animals off site. Several residents have photographs of deformed cows. (31) In the early 1990s tumors were found in fish in the Scioto River. The Ohio EPA tests found elevated levels of radiation in the fish, five times normal radiation in the stream sediments, as well as arsenic, cadmium, chromium and mercury. (32) A 2007 Ohio EPA report said that technetium levels were dropping in the streams, though an independent analysis commissioned by a local environmental group showed levels of radium 100 times normal levels in two spots in Big Run. (33)

iii

As at Paducah, there was extensive chemical contamination of the soil and groundwater at Piketon, particularly from the solvent chemical Trichloroethylene (TCE), which had been used to clean the equipment of the cascades. The chemical contamination at Piketon, in fact, has long been considered one of its most dangerous problems. TCE was found to have seeped into one of the two aquifers beneath the plant. The DOE claims that the shallow aquifer beneath the plant, which is badly contaminated, had no effect on area drinking water, and that the deep aquifer is clean. Other scientists say they may be speaking too soon, that migration of TCE into the vicinity of the larger aquifer could be taking place. Five groundwater plumes, identified beneath the plant site, contained TCE, technetium and uranium. There are also cracks in the bedrock of the aquifer, which means that at some time there could be toxic leaks into the soil. (34) In 1999 the DOE tried to loosen the rules governing the cleanup of the TCE-- to reduce costs-- but the Ohio EPA refused. (35)

Another serious chemical contaminant at Piketon was hexavalent chromium, which up to 1989 had been added to the water in the cooling tower to prevent wood corrosion. (This is the highly toxic chemical Erin Brockovich, subject of the movie, investigated.) In fact, in 1988 when the DOE made its first ranking of environmental problems at all the nuclear weapons plants, Piketon, because of the chromium, was at the top of the list. (36) In 1991 the DOE reported that 860 pounds of chromium and 140,000 pounds of chlorine had been released into the air via the stacks of the cooling tower and 710 pounds released into the Scioto River. (37) Like TCE, it is a proven carcinogen which can cause kidney, liver and respiratory disease. Highly toxic PCBs were in the water as well. The 2007 Ohio EPA report on water quality at Piketon said that the levels of PCBs in the streams were as high as they had been in 1992 when the quality tests were first done. The PCBs, also carcinogenic, are evidently coming from contaminated waste oil drained from electrical transformers in the 1980s. (38)

The most serious accident at the plant occurred on March 7, 1978, when a cylinder of hot liquid uranium hexafluoride was accidentally dropped ten inches and ruptured, creating an eight-inch long split in the tank. The contents of the cylinder-- over 20,000 pounds of uranium hexafluoride--were released into the atmosphere and into the local creeks. (39) According to the *Dayton Daily News*, workers had repeatedly warned the plant operators about the carriers, but had not been listened to. When the rupture occurred, workers first tried to stop the leak by putting tarps and sandbags on the cylinder. When this didn't work, a truck driver named Kenny Estep (untrained in emergency procedures) was asked to dump snow on the cylinder, which he did for the next 30 minutes. By the time the leak was stopped, over 10,000 pounds of uranium had been carried off in a toxic airborne plume; at least 1,500 pounds of uranium had escaped through a drainage pipe into the Scioto River, which flows into the Ohio. Estep told his wife that night about the "green poison" he had seen in the snow. "That was dangerous what we done tonight. They really panicked." (Estep himself died of a rare form of liver cancer seven years later at the age of 42.) (40) The plant manager's report about the incident described the releases as "routine," and many of the workers were not even told what had happened. In 1980 a government study ruled that Piketon had had over 111 *significant* radioactive releases over the years, more than either of the enrichment plants at Paducah and Oak Ridge. (41)

When we toured the plant in the winter of 2004, a worker told us that she had heard rumors that a whole factory had been dismantled and buried somewhere on plant grounds, though plant managers denied it. A report of the Yggdrasil Institute, however, confirmed this story, that an INCO (International Nickel Company) plant in Huntington, West Virginia (60 miles away from Piketon) had been buried in the Classified Materials Disposal Facility. (42) A web search revealed that INCO, a large defense contractor, had built the Huntington Pilot Plant in 1951 to provide nickel for the barriers of the cascades at Paducah and Piketon. To save money, INCO had used scrap nickel from K-25 in Oak Ridge, but this nickel was already contaminated with uranium. The Huntington plant closed in 1963, but was not dismantled until 1979; all the radioactive debris was then secretly shipped to Piketon. (No environmental impact study of the nickel burial has ever been done.) Today former workers at INCO--and their survivors--are, like the enrichment workers, trying to receive compensation for their unwitting radiation exposure. (43) (Incidents such as these resulted in the federal ban of the sale of contaminated metals in 2000, the ban which Paducah officials are now trying to get overturned in order to sell their contaminated nickel.)

By the mid-1960s the need for enriched uranium for military purposes began to lessen, because of the glut of nuclear weapons in the American arsenal. The competition between the American and Soviet leaders as to who could have the most nuclear bombs had resulted in both countries having lopsided military economies, huge nuclear stockpiles, mountains of waste, sick workers, and badly contaminated landscapes. (According to *Nuclear Wastelands,* the monumental study of radioactive waste throughout the world, Russia's contamination appears to be severe, though many health and environmental records continue to be concealed.) (44)   In the late 1960s Piketon stopped enriching uranium for weapons and began to produce fuel only for commercial nuclear power plants, enriching the low-level uranium from Paducah up to 5-6%. Piketon also continued to receive uranium from Oak Ridge, which it enriched up to 97% for the submarine reactors.

iv

In 1969 Nixon proposed selling the three gaseous diffusion plants to private industry. He said he didn't foresee the government needing much nuclear material for defense in the future--an interesting position--and the aging gaseous diffusion plants were an enormous drain on the federal budget. (45) His proposal, however, wasn't accepted by the AEC. Instead the AEC began aggressively to promote the development of civilian nuclear power plants throughout the world, then selling American enriched uranium to them, under a little known or supervised operation known as the "Uranium Enrichment Enterprise." At the time the AEC had a monopoly of enriched uranium in the non-communist world. Private companies in Europe and Japan as well as the United States submitted feed uranium to Paducah and Piketon, where it was enriched and made fissionable. (46) In time, however, the international uranium deals of the AEC became a source of public concern. In late 1977 it was disclosed that radioactive materials were being shipped by truck on the highways from Piketon to Chicago, where they were then being sent abroad to the countries of Europe and Asia. When he learned this, the mayor of Chicago immediately banned shipment of nuclear materials out of O'Hare. (47)

From 1974 to 1981 major plant upgrades and improvements occurred, in part in response to the demands of labor and environmentalists. In 1971 the Clean Air Act had been passed by Congress to control emissions of ash and sulfur dioxide, which were causing acid rain. Power plants were told to switch to coal with lower sulfur content, to install "scrubbers" to clean the sulfur components from emissions, or to build tall stacks to push exhaust plume fumes further out into the atmosphere. Piketon chose the third option because it was cheapest. (48) Not until 30 years later did the Indiana-Kentucky Electricity Corporation finally agree to build a $460 million scrubber to reduce coal emissions from the plant at Clifty Creek. (49)

In the late 1970s Jimmy Carter proposed replacing the gaseous diffusion plant at Piketon with a new centrifuge model which would use only a fraction of the electricity--and coal. The centrifuge operates something like a cream separator: its rotating cylinders create a strong centrifugal force which draws the heavier U-238 molecules to the outside, while the lighter U-235 molecules collect near the center. In the early 1970s Oak Ridge had experimented with centrifuges, but had had numerous mechanical failures, including one major accident in 1973. (50) As part of his presidential campaign pledge, however, Carter had promised to bring a centrifuge plant (and jobs) to Ohio. (51)

Fluor Enterprises was hired to build the centrifuge plant at Piketon, but six years later, after spending $2.6 billion on the installation, the plant closed. The reasons for the closure were never made clear, though they may have had to do with the uncertain future of nuclear power. According to the *New York Times,* the DOE said in 1985 it had simply changed its mind, and was going to return to research on the isotope separation method of enrichment. (52) During the next 25 years the government quietly spent over two *billion* dollars on the isotope separation method, but couldn't get it to work either. (53) Thus both Piketon and Paducah continued with the very expensive, very polluting, gaseous diffusion method. The centrifuges from the 1980's were dismantled and hauled to the Nevada Test Site, where they were buried in a landfill for secret garbage. (54)

In 1986 Goodyear Atomic was finally replaced, and Martin Marietta Energy Systems took over management of both the Paducah and Piketon plants. It was in the late 1980s that the contamination at both facilities finally came to light. At first the federal government refused to consider complying with EPA standards at Piketon, invoking "sovereign immunity," meaning essentially the federal government can do what it wants. Unlike the state of Kentucky, however, the state of Ohio decided to take on the federal government, not wanting to get stuck with the massive Piketon cleanup costs. Pressured by Ohio Attorney General Anthony Celebrezze, Senator John Glenn, and Cincinnati Congressman Tom Luken, the DOE eventually agreed to spend $50 million to bring the plant into compliance with Ohio environmental law. (55) In 1991 the DOE suspended production of highly enriched uranium for naval ships at Piketon. With the end of the cold war, as well as the waning enthusiasm for nuclear power, it seemed there would be much less demand for enriched uranium in the future.

In 1986 the Reagan cabinet had talked about privatizing the gaseous enrichment plants, in the words of one advisor, "selling the whole shebang," (56) but a clean sale never took place. Instead in 1992 the DOE established a rather murky arrangement with a new company, the United States Enrichment Corporation (USEC), which essentially developed out of the old Uranium Enrichment Enterprise. (57) According to the new arrangement, the DOE (that is, taxpayers) would support USEC until it could financially make it on its own. A Wall

Street banker, William Timbers, who as a consultant had initially recommended the forming of USEC, was hired as its president/CEO. USEC assumed management of both Paducah and Piketon. As an indication of where USEC's values were, however, one of its first acts was to meet with the officials of Martin Marietta, and the two corporations secretly erased 464 computer records having to do with open safety issues at the plants. These erasures were done without clearance from the Department of Energy. So severe were some of the missing violations that the DOE considered closing both plants, but in the end didn't, and the corporations were not even fined. (58)

v

Piketon workers, however, were beginning to speak up. In 1980 two film-makers interviewed union workers and their families, and produced a documentary for British television called *For My Working Life*. In the film Piketon workers spoke openly about their fears of radiation exposures, leukemia in young workers, and accidents and careless oversight at the plant. They acknowledged, though, that most workers were afraid to speak up for fear of losing their clearance and jobs. Two FBI men, they said, were known to circulate in the community and listen to what people were saying. (59) In the late 1980s, early 1990s a local group called PRESS (Piketon/ Portsmouth Residents for Environmental Safety and Security) came into being, part of an emerging network, National Nuclear Workers for Justice. Tom Wilkerson, a resident in the area, was an early spokesperson, but later Vina Colley, a former worker at the plant, became its outspoken president.

Unions also became more vocal. In 1979 members of the Oil, Chemical and Atomic Workers union put pressure on Washington to investigate the problems at Piketon, and asked specifically for a NIOSH health study on worker exposure to uranium hexafluoride. Eventually this study was done. (A study was not done at Paducah; it was thought that Piketon workers might be in more danger because of the higher level of the enrichment there, a point I have not seen discussed elsewhere.) (60) In 1987 NIOSH released the results of its study of the Piketon workers, and though the report showed elevated numbers for stomach cancer and leukemia, the authors of the study said these cancers were not "statistically significant." According to Robert Alvarez, who analyzed the report, the NIOSH study was of limited usefulness because it had used a young cohort (group of individuals studied), had a flawed life-table analysis, and had had to rely on insufficient and unreliable plant data about radiation releases ("exposure metrics leaves much to be desired"). (61) Larry Elliott, today compensation director at NIOSH, said that in some cases patient records were "modified or changed by the DOE." A later NIOSH report in 2001 also only studied dead workers, leaving about 85% of the workforce out of the report. (62)

In 1994 residents living near the plant completed their own informal cancer survey, going house-to-house, finding out about cancers of people who lived there, whom they knew about, or who had died or moved away. They identified

247 cancer cases within a six mile radius of the plant, the majority in Pike County. Investigators from Boston University also looked into cancers in the area, talking with a Pike County public health nurse who commented on the unusually high number of childhood cancers, and an oncologist in Chillicothe who reported unusual malignancies. (63) The DOE dismissed these personal stories as anecdotal and inconclusive--though given that the government's own epidemiological studies were based on insufficient data, if not fabrications, it's hard to see their position as much more tenable.

The Public Health Assessment report of the federal ATSDR (Agency for Toxic Substances and Disease Registry)-- part of the Center for Disease Control in Atlanta-- contains a transcript of one of the public hearings in the mid 1990s when Piketon workers and residents were given the opportunity to ask questions about the NIOSH report and express their health concerns. To almost every question, the ATSDR officials replied that their evidence showed "no health hazards" at Piketon. An early report which had shown a high technetium count in an offsite well was dismissed because it had simply been a "typographical error." Black residue which covered trees, houses and cars in the vicinity of the plant was probably "sap from nearby trees." Lung cancers were due to smoking. Local fish were not contaminated. Arsenic was not used at the plant, but probably came from "pesticides used on fruit trees." Studies which showed unusually high rates of cancer in southeastern Ohio were dismissed as statistically flawed. At one point someone in the audience asked about the conversion plant in X705. "Was plutonium ever processed, used or stored at the Portsmouth plant?" Answer: "Plutonium was never worked with at the Portsmouth facility." (64) It had been, of course; the officials were lying. It's not hard to see why the people of Piketon today are so skeptical of government hearings and reports. In 2000 Kenneth Brooks, a former safety manager at Piketon, revealed that he had been fired for refusing to conceal problems at the plant and delete items from a safety data base. He said he had filed a whistleblower lawsuit in 1996, requesting relevant documents from the DOE through the Freedom of Information Act, but didn't hear back from the DOE for five years, long after his claim had been dismissed. (65)

After the *Washington Post* disclosures about Paducah in the fall of 1999, Representative Ted Strickland of Lucasville, as well as Ohio Senators Mike DeWine and George Voinovich, held a public hearing for Piketon workers and residents. About 150 people crowded into a motel conference room and testified for four hours about their health concerns. Stanley McNally, a janitor, told about being in a restroom when an accident occurred and a siren sounded. He ran out into a "white solid fog," holding his breath as long as he could, but finally the steam went down his throat. He developed cancer a year later. Anita George, an employee for 23 years, said many women workers had questions about their reproductive health. She knew of only one female co-worker in her department, she said, who had not had a hysterectomy or some other problem such as a miscarriage or infertility. A Quality Assurance investigator named Terry Adams, who had been sent to Piketon to look for problems, said that when he reported barrels of lithium hydroxide leaking into the Scioto River, he had been "demoted for telling the truth." He said later, "We found a lot of things we didn't like. We had some hair-raising reports because there had been no (previous) documentation." (66)

Stories of illnesses became more common. A man who had worked from 1975-1988 disconnecting the tanks of UF6 was diagnosed with severe lung damage. He was 36. (67) A chemical operator at the plant from 1975-1985 died of brain cancer at the age of 46. (68) One of the Piketon security guards, Jeffery Waldron, became sick after inhaling a vaporous cloud of unknown origin in 1994. Today he is losing the lining of his lungs. Waldron testified before Congress in 1999 that he had evidence plant officials had routinely altered and falsified records of radiation exposures. (69) Though he is still working at the plant, his lungs continue to bubble.

Sam Ray, a former worker, testified at Senate hearings in 2000. Ray had worked at Piketon from 1954-1994 as a mechanic and production operator until he contracted a rare form of bone cancer (chondrosarcoma) and had to have his larynx removed. (He spoke with a voice amplifier.) He told his own story and those of fellow workers who had not been protected against exposures. Robert Elkins, who had worked in X705 from 1962 till 1965, had been placed on permanent work restriction because of his high body count. Though he was never contacted by plant officials after his retirement years later, he *was* contacted (like William Flint, the worker at Mound) by a researcher at Hanford, who offered $500 for his corpse when he died, and $500 for his wife, too. (They refused.) Ray said he knew of 17 workers who had been found with excessive levels of radiation in their lungs, and 11 of them had worked in X705. (70) (Ray himself died of multiple cancers in May, 2007.)

In the early 2000s it was discovered that eight Piketon workers were suffering from chronic beryllium disease; ten others tested sensitive to it. Initially the DOE said there had been no beryllium at Piketon, only at Paducah, but later had to retract their statement, for in 2004 records revealed unexpectedly high levels of beryllium on the aluminum blades in the giant compressors. How the beryllium got to Piketon isn't clear. Gary Saxton, a chemical operator and union representative, was one of those diagnosed with beryllium disease, which scars the lungs and can be fatal. (71)

In 1999 the *Cincinnati Enquirer* reported that Pike County had the highest death rate of any county in Ohio. The reporter, however, attributed the deaths to the "poverty" of Appalachian culture. Nowhere in the (lengthy) article is there a mention of the uranium enrichment plant. (72)

vi

In 1995 USEC had announced it was going to begin "downblending" the highly enriched uranium which had been destined for use in naval reactors, and convert it into fuel for civilian nuclear power plants. President Clinton promoted "downblending" in order to encourage other countries to do the same with their bomb-grade material. DOE Secretary Hazel O'Leary said the aim of the "Megatons to Megawatts Project" was "to recycle weapons materials for peaceful purposes." (73) The Clinton administration gave USEC 50 metric tons of highly enriched uranium to get started with the conversion (that is, mixing the high level uranium with depleted uranium to bring down the enrichment level). By the summer of 2006 USEC reported that it had successfully converted these 50 tons into fuel for nuclear power plants. (74) USEC was also given the responsibility of taking in uranium from Russia, which the first Bush administration had agreed to purchase and downgrade, as a way of getting rid of Russian nuclear warheads, preventing old bomb-grade material from falling into terrorists' hands, and establishing a positive working relationship with the Russian nuclear industry. (75)

By the late 1990s, however, USEC was economically struggling: with all the American as well as the Russian uranium on its hands, prices fell. USEC was also now competing with enrichment plants in other parts of the world, particularly URENCO in Europe. In 1998 the government was faced with the decision either to sell USEC to a private business group, or to allow USEC itself to become a for-profit corporation (with Timbers again at the head). The DOE did the latter. Then-Representative Ted Strickland (now governor of Ohio) said, "It was a deal made to enrich insiders...the most frustrating experience I've ever had with the government." (76) The resulting private company, USEC Inc., was given leasing rights at Piketon with virtually no federal regulation or community oversight. To sell its stock on Wall Street, USEC Inc. let it be known it was in the process of developing a new method of isotope enrichment: the Atomic Vapor Laser Isotope Separator (AVLIS). There were still fears, however, that the USEC shares wouldn't sell. (According to the *New York Times*, the NRC changed the date of its regulatory hearings dealing with health and safety issues until after all the shares were sold, so that investors wouldn't know of all the contamination problems at Paducah and Piketon). (77) Also, after all the shares were sold, USEC announced that it was abandoning AVLIS (there were still too many technical difficulties). Two stockholders a few years later tried to sue USEC for fraud, but lost their case.

In June, 2000 USEC suddenly announced it was closing Piketon to concentrate all the uranium enrichment at Paducah. There was an angry outcry, for when USEC had been privatized it had been with the stipulation that it would not close either Paducah or Piketon before 2005. A small print clause in the contract, however, had said if USEC's credit rating was downgraded to below investment grade it could. At the time the plant employed about 2,000 people. The average salary, with benefits, of those affected by the closing was $49,000, nearly double the wage of most Pike County residents. (78) Some talked about leaving, moving to Columbus or Cincinnati. All were fearful about their futures. Said one worker: "For me to be filling out a resume right now is difficult. No one wants to hire a former nuclear worker. They're worried about our health and their insurance premiums." (79)

Four months later, though, in October, 2000, USEC announced that Piketon would go on "steady standby" status and not close completely, which meant the company could continue to collect contract fees for its "operation." Rumors began to circulate that USEC might revive the old centrifuge plant at Piketon. In the next year, as the pro-war, pro-nuclear and anti-environmental forces became powerful in the new Bush administration, uranium enrichment again looked like it had a future, so USEC announced it *would* build a new centrifuge plant at either Piketon or Paducah, and went to both state governments to solicit "incentive" money. Ohio put up $125 million dollars in tax abatements and eventually won the site selection. (It was probably the preferred site all along, since it had started the centrifuge program back in the 1980s. Fluor said, in fact, in 2004, once the decision was announced, that it was simply coming back to "help finish a project we began 25 years ago.") (80)

USEC announced that the new plant would be called American Centrifuge, because it would be based on an (untested) American design, be "principally US sourced," and installation would be conducted by "highly qualified American companies." USEC said it would first build a $150 million dollar test facility, the Lead Cascade, with 240 centrifuges, to demonstrate how well the system worked; with its success, it would then be able to get the funding for the complete operation which would cost $1 to 1.5 billion and bring in 500 permanent jobs. After American Centrifuge opened in 2010, Timbers said, Paducah would permanently close. (81)

Timbers' calling the plant American Centrifuge was in part to differentiate it from *another* uranium enrichment plant, LES, being built in New Mexico, which is 70% owned by the European energy conglomerate URENCO. (USEC tried to block the Europeans from the American market through a lawsuit in 2000, but failed.) (82) URENCO has already built centrifuge plants of its own design in England, Holland and Germany. Also one of URENCO's former employees, A.Q. Khan of Pakistan, (illegally) took the centrifuge plans and supposedly has sold them to several countries in Asia and the Middle East, including Iran. The URENCO American company first tried to build the centrifuge plant in Louisiana and Tennessee, but local communities at both places opposed it. It was "welcomed" later, however, by the small town of Eunice, New Mexico, which badly wanted the jobs. The URENCO company, now called the National Enrichment Facility, received its NRC license to operate the LES centrifuge in 2006, (83) and has already acquired purchase contracts from Westinghouse, Entergy, Exetor and Duke Energy. (84) Environmentalists, however, have raised many questions about the New Mexico plant having to do with geologic fractures which could lead to contamination of underground waterways, and the lack of adequate plans for dealing with the tons of new depleted uranium waste which will be generated. (85)

vi

At the end of 2007, three major operations were going on at the Piketon site. One was the DOE remediation of the old site, which though initially contracted to Bechtel-Jacobs, was later in the hands of two smaller companies, LATA and Parallax. Several treatment facilities were built to remove the trichloroethylene and other chemical contaminants from the water. According to the *Dayton Daily News,* the TCE remains the most pervasive groundwater contaminant at Piketon, and the companies are having difficulty removing it. One of the five plumes on the edge of the plant seems to have contaminated a monitoring well on a farm nearby. (86) Some of the radioactive equipment has been buried. Mixed waste and sludge (both radioactive and chemical) has been sent to Energy Solutions (formerly Envirocare) in Utah; low-level radioactive waste has been sent to Hanford, Washington, and liquid toxic waste to an incinerator in Oak Ridge. Some of the radioactive waste still in the landfills at Piketon will, according to *Danger Lurks Below,* always be there and "will require maintenance, essentially forever." (87) It's not known at this time what will happen to the three massive gaseous diffusion buildings. The Ohio EPA would like to see the buildings cleaned and demolished and the debris removed, but the DOE wants to leave the buildings standing. It has put no money for their demolition in its five-year cleanup plan, which has led to rumors it plans to use them for other unknown purposes. Beyerlein and Hulsey said in their report, "What dangers lie beneath the thick concrete floors of those [cascade] buildings is anybody's guess." (88)

UDS (Uranium Disposition Services) is in the process of building a conversion plant at Piketon, as it is at Paducah, to try to get rid of the barrels of depleted uranium. As of 2007, the construction of the plant was not very far along. If and when the conversion plant goes into operation, it will take nearly 20 years to get rid of all the DU at Piketon. The plan to extract hydrofluoric acid from the DU for resale is also now jeopardized by the possibility that the uranium was contaminated with plutonium, and by the residue from the chemical gas phosgene. (89) On our tour of the Piketon plant in 2004, we were told that the uranium oxide residue from the conversion will eventually be sent "somewhere," but it may also simply stay on site, a source of great worry to residents. This uranium oxide residue will continue to be radioactive for billions of years. The gaseous diffusion plant at Oak Ridge, now shut down, has also shipped some of its barrels of depleted uranium to Piketon. The rusty, potentially leaking, cylinders, each weighing 14 tons, were moved by truck the 300 miles from Oak Ridge to Ohio. On January 9, 2000 a car hit one of these trucks hauling two 20-ton uranium canisters through Chillicothe, Ohio. USEC said the canisters were empty and that they did not rupture; (90) still, the danger of the transport of these cylinders is a source of great concern.

In 2000 a Uranium Management Center was set up in Piketon to handle different kinds of waste being brought in. Some waste from Fernald and Hanford was even brought to Piketon for "temporary" storage (simply to help the operators meet their cleanup deadlines and get the remediation bonuses). The Uranium Management Center tried to sell some of this waste, but Steve Schutt of Nuclear Fuel Services of Tennessee said that 40% of the stockpile was tested and found to be "useless," so it will apparently remain in Piketon. (91) In 2004 four cylinders of uranium hexafluoride --as well as other nuclear material-- arrived in Piketon from Libya, raising fears that Piketon could become a massive nuclear dump not only for the country but for the world. (92)

The third major operation now going on at Piketon is USEC's troubled effort to complete plans for the American Centrifuge. Late in 2003 William Timbers was fired as CEO (he sued and received $15 million in compensation) (93), and though no reasons were given for his firing, industry journals indicated there were problems with the centrifuge project and USEC in general. For one thing the date for the trial run of the Lead Cascade kept getting postponed. Some tests apparently went on in the fall of 2007, but the Lead Cascade has not proven to be the technological success USEC had hoped. One nuclear scientist said, "The bigger the centrifuge, the harder it is to build. This is a really big one. Compared with Russian or European designs, it's like spinning a toothpick versus a telephone pole." (94) How safe the new design will be is also uncertain. In 2005 the Nuclear Regulatory Commission approved USEC's request to keep secret part of its license application, including safety and accident analyses, so local residents simply couldn't find out the dangers the new plant might entail. (95)

The most serious problem facing USEC today, however, is that it is heavily in debt. Its own uranium stockpile is gone; the utility bills from Paducah continue to be astronomical; the Russians are wanting out of their deal with USEC so they can sell directly to U.S. utilities; and the Lead Cascade itself has cost three times what was projected. (96) Most significant of all, USEC has not been able to raise the money needed to build the American Centrifuge itself (the new estimate is that it would cost $2.5 billion, perhaps more, up from the originally projected $1.7 billion). (97) Throughout early 2007 USEC scrambled to come up with financing plans (spending over a $1.8 million in lobbying fees in the first half of 2007 alone). (98) One plan was to get the DOE to "give them" all the depleted uranium at Paducah and Piketon (worth over $2 billion), which they would then convert for use in nuclear power plants, a plan which was met with both congressional and scientific skepticism. In the fall of 2007 it was revealed that Energy Solutions (formerly Envirocare) had submitted a proposal to the Department of Energy to take over USEC, *if* the federal government would give Energy Solutions a single source $9.5 *billion* contract for the "decontamination and decommissioning" of both Paducah and Piketon. With this government contract, Energy Solutions/ USEC would then have the funds to go ahead with the American Centrifuge. The DOE didn't like this proposal, however, and in the fall of 2007 turned it down. Rep. John Dingell applauded the DOE decision, saying the single source contract for the cleanup was a bad deal for the American taxpayers, and seemed also to be an indirect way for USEC to get federal money to bail out the Centrifuge. (99) At the end of 2007, however, it looked like USEC had managed to get federal bailout money after all. Senator Peter Domenici of New Mexico, the nuclear industry's most ardent proponent, had managed to slip a $2 billion loan guarantee for enrichment plants into the 2005 Energy Bill. When anti-nuclear activists and congressional leaders discovered what he had done, they had it removed, but in 2007 (just before his retirement) Domenici slipped the $2 billion loan guarantee into the Appropriations Bill, which funds government operations. (100) Because the Appropriations Bill passed, it appears the loan guarantee is in place, but legal battles may still lie ahead. In the past Senator George Voinovich of Ohio has said he would oppose a taxpayer bailout for USEC (101), but thus far he has been silent about the Appropriations Bill funding ploy.

Even if USEC never does get the American Centrifuge to become operational, it's possible another corporation could step in. In July, 2007 the French energy conglomerate Areva (which is 80% owned by the French government) announced that it would build a centrifuge in the United States some time in the next decade, (102) and local residents fear it may be eyeing Piketon. A *CNN* story in August, 2007 indicated that BWXT, formerly Babcock and Wilcox-- which had once operated Mound--has a factory in Mt. Vernon, Indiana, on the

Ohio River, and plans to team up with Areva to build vessels for reactors. (103) Despite media reports that France is a "model" nuclear country, it has not figured out what to do with its waste either. Some of its liquid radioactive waste has been discharged into the English Channel, permanent repositories for depleted uranium, reprocessing waste, and spent fuel rods from power plants still do not exist, and many French people are as afraid of the temporary disposal sites as Americans are. (104) In the late 90s a group called Meres en Colere (Angry Mothers) was formed when high levels of childhood leukemia were found near the nuclear waste disposal site near Beaumont-Hague. (105)

viii

The government, nuclear industry and some local political and business leaders are putting great pressure on the job-starved residents to allow these new nuclear plans to be developed in Piketon. In 1995 the Department of Energy gave $15 million to a group of local businessmen to form SODI (the Southern Ohio Diversification Initiative), supposedly its "community partner" at Piketon, though it is a private development corporation, and its meetings and minutes are closed to the public. In 2001 USEC gave SODI another $2 million to plan the site's "redevelopment." In 2004 USEC purchased NAC International, a company which specializes in the storage of high-level nuclear waste. (106) It is this final possibility which is alarming local residents a great deal at the present time. Spent fuel rods from nuclear power plants, as said before, are the most dangerous nuclear waste there is, containing plutonium and other transuranic elements. The government is in a huge expensive quandary about what to do about the fuel rods. A law passed by Congress in 1998 made the DOE obligated to find a permanent location for them, but they haven't managed to do so. The planned permanent repository at Yucca Mountain in Nevada has faced many scientific and political objections. The DOE tried to build an "interim" storage site in Skull Valley, Utah, but residents objected there too, fearing the "interim" might become permanent. (107) Fifty-six utility companies have sued the DOE for failure to find a location for the spent fuel, since they are still being forced to pay for storage, liability, and security; the courts have ordered the DOE to pay out billions to the utility companies. Instead of investing in a program to strengthen the security of the cooling ponds where the fuel rods are presently kept--the view of many scientists that this would be the safest solution to the problem of past radioactive waste--the DOE is apparently looking for another "interim" storage site, possibly Piketon. Having spent fuel rods at Piketon would mean the most deadly radioactive waste on earth would be regularly transported on public highways from all over the country, with no guarantee of its safety, health or environmental impact. There would also not be any assurance it wouldn't remain on the Scioto River forever. (108)

In 2006 SODI joined forces with a wealthy Cleveland developer named Dan T. Moore III to form SONIC (the Southern Ohio Nuclear Integration Cooperative). Moore was formerly on the board of USEC, and an advisor to SONIC is a former USEC manager. (109) On November 29, 2006 it was announced that SONIC would receive a $673,761 federal grant, as part of George W. Bush's

GNEP (Global Nuclear Energy Partnership) to study the feasibility of some kind of new nuclear facility at Piketon. Congress slashed the GNEP budget by 73%--which perhaps means that a reprocessing plant is not an immediate possibility--but Piketon is apparently still being regarded for other things, possibly an "interim" dump.

The specific plans of SONIC, however, are being kept secret from the community. One angry resident, Tressie Hall, who lives a half a mile from the old plant, said, "They think we're dumb because we're poor and they can just pull anything over on us they want." (110) The residents, however, are becoming increasingly vocal. A local group SONG (Southern Ohio Neighbors Group) has collected over 5,000 signatures of residents who are opposed to the location being used as a storage space for spent fuel. Members of SONG, PRESS, and others worried about the secret nuclear plans for Piketon would like to form a federally-sanctioned Citizens Advisory Board (CAB) which would allow citizen input about the cleanup and the future use of the site. The Federal Advisory Committee Act (FACA) enacted by Congress in 1972 has strict requirements about the composition of the board, its powers, and its recommendations, which are legally binding. (Piketon is one of the few nuclear facilities which has never had a CAB, one of the reasons, residents feel, that the DOE felt it could come in without any organized community resistance.) SODI is trying to propose an alternative, informal "community advisory committee" with its own selected members, which would not be hampered by the rules and regulations of FACA. It is the legal rules and regulations, however, which the residents of Piketon want. A DOE hearing about the various CAB proposals is scheduled for the spring of 2008. (111)

As for the workers, still living, who once took part in the old gaseous diffusion operation, their attempts to receive compensation are proceeding slowly. As of the fall of 2006 only 28% of the Piketon workers, and survivors of workers, who had submitted health claims had received compensation through the Energy Employee Occupational Illness Compensation Program. (112) In June, 2007 Ohio Senators George Voinovich and Sherrod Brown both called for a congressional oversight hearing to investigate why so few workers were receiving compensation. (113) In the summer of 2007 a federal judge also allowed the case to proceed of the Piketon area residents who have filed damage claims because of all the chemical contamination. Cincinnati attorney Stanley Chesley, handling the case, said, "We're going to get to the bottom of this, to the truth, just like we did at Fernald, which was covered up for years." (114) Like the sick workers at Paducah, Mound and Fernald, however, the workers at Piketon still wonder if they will live long enough to receive any of the benefits.

The long-term effect of the radiation and chemicals on workers, residents and the environment at Piketon is still far from certain. Even if the area is not turned into a high- level waste disposal site, even if no centrifuge or reprocessing plant becomes operational in the future, monitoring and testing will have to continue in some form at Piketon for centuries to come. It is no wonder the residents are worried. The coils of the nearby serpent are an eerie reminder of the forces of death as well as life.

Notes: Piketon

1. "Rock Samples From Beneath Mound Contain Rare Metal," *Associated Press State and Local Wire,* April 17, 2005.

2. Adkins, Thomas, "A Brief History of Pike County." Website of Pike County Chamber of Commerce. (www.pikechamber.org/history.html)

3. "Cincinnati Atom Plant a Billion Dollar Stomach Ache," *Cincinnati Enquirer,* April 20, 1952, 6.

4. Sea, Geoffrey. "A Brief Chronology of the U.S. Government Community Relations at the Piketon Federal Reservation." Website of SONG (Southern Ohio Neighbors Group). (http://ohioneighbors.org/shipp.aspx)

5. "Demure Little Pike: She's A Boom Belle Now," *Cincinnati Enquirer,* August 14, 1952, 11.

6. Radioactive Waste Management Associates, *Danger Lurks Below: The Threat to Major Water Suppliers from the US DOE Nuclear Weapons Plants* (Washington, D.C.: Alliance for Nuclear Accountability, 2004), 168. (www.ananuclear.org)

7. "Demure" 11.

8. Trussell, C. P., "$1,200,000,000 Atom Plant to Be Built in Southern Ohio," *New York Times,* August 13, 1952, 1.

9. Finney, John W., "Johnson Orders Reduction in Nuclear Arms Output," *New York Times,* January 9, 1964, 1.

10. "Atomic Land Rush Sweeps Ohio Hills," *New York Times,* August 15, 1952, 28.

11. "Sacred Prehistoric Sites of Sargents: The Alembic." Website of SONG (Southern Ohio Neighbors Group) (http://ohioneighbors.org/shipp.aspx)

12. "Portsmouth: Plant History," Website of USEC (United States Enrichment Corporation) (http://www.usec.com/v2001_02/html/facilities_portshistory.asp)

13. "Plant Operations Modified by A.E.C.: Union Carbide & Carbon to Run Additional Facilities Now Under Construction," *New York Times,* September 2, 1953, 40.

14. Davis, Mary Byrd, "A Guide to Key Facilities and Sites at the Portsmouth Gaseous Diffusion Plant," Yggdrasil Institute: Uranium Enrichment Project. Website of Earth Island Institute. (www.earthisland.org/yggdrasil/portsmouth_gdp.html)

15. Hulsey, Lynn and Tom Beyerlein, "Piketon: A Troubled Past," *Dayton Daily News,* November 12, 2006.

16. Davis, "A Guide."

17. Hulsey and Beyerlein, "Piketon: A Troubled Past."

18. Hulsey and Beyerlein, "Piketon: A Troubled Past."

19. Dela Merced, Lynn. "Initial Review of the Environmental Impacts of the Portsmouth Gaseous Diffusion Plant," Yggdrasil Institute: Report for PRESS and the Uranium Enrichment Project. October, 2000. (www.earthisland.org/yggdrasil/uep_11_04.html)

20. Davis, "A Guide."

21. "Cleanup Chronology," *Dayton Daily News,* December 7, 2006.

22. Ray, Sam, "Testimony at Senate Hearing." September 21, 2000. Website of GlobalSecurity.org. (http://www.globalsecurity.org/wmd/library/congress/2000_h/ray0921.htm)

23. Beyerlein, Tom, and Lynn Hulsey, "Workers Fight for Compensation," *Dayton Daily News,* November 13, 2006.

24. Beyerlein, Tom and Lynn Hulsey,. "Rare Skin Disorder Haunts Man After Radioactive Release," *Dayton Daily News,* November 12, 2006.

25. Dela Merced.

26. Ray.

27. Davis, "A Guide."

28. Dela Merced.

29. Dela Merced.

30. Hintermann, Beat, Marilynn Dela Merced and Marvin Resnikoff.   Radioactive Waste Management Associates. "Groundwater Movement at the Portsmouth Gaseous Diffusion Plant." Yggdrasil Institute: Report for PRESS and the Uranium Enrichment Project, February, 2002. (www.earthisland.org/yggdrasil/pgdp.html)

31. Personal interview with Tressie Hall, Janaury 19, 2008.

32. "Radiation Up in Fish Near Uranium Plant," *Cleveland Plain Dealer,* February 8, 1993, 3B.

33. Lafferty, Mike, "Radioactivity Low in Streams Near Piketon Plant," *Columbus Dispatch,* February 1, 2007.

34. Radioactive Waste Management 169.

35. Hulsey and Beyerlein, "Piketon: A Troubled Past."

36. Wald, Matthew L., "Blowing, Flowing and Crawling, Nature is Spreading Nuclear Waste.," *New York Times,* December 10, 1988, 10.

37. Davis, "A Guide."

38. Lafferty.

39. Coyle, D., L. Finaldi, E. Greenfield, M. Hamilton, E. Hedemann, W. McDonnell, M. Resnikoff, J. Scarlotti and J. Tichenor, *Deadly Defense: Military Radioactive Landfills. A Citizen's Guide* (New York: Radioactive Waste Campaign, 1988), 86.

40. Hulsey, Lynn and Tom Beyerlein, "Ill-Equipped Workers Frantically Tried to Stop Toxic Leak," *Dayton Daily News,* November 13, 2006.

41. "Cleanup Chronology."

42. Davis, Mary Byrd, "Excerpts from *Uranium Enrichment Establishment,1999.* Published by the Uranium Enrichment Project of Earth Island's Yggdrasil Institute. August 9, 1999. (www.earthisland.org/yggdrasil/uranium.html)

43. Wartman, Scott, "Remnants of Cold War: Secret Plant's Legacy Still Debated," *Huntington Herald-Dispatch,* April 10, 2005, 1A.

44. Makhijani, Arjun, Howard Hu and Katherine Yih, editors, *Nuclear Wastelands: A Global Guide to Nuclear Weapons Production and Its Health and Environmental Effects* (Cambridge, Mass: MIT Press, 2000), 285-392.

45. Semple, Jr., Robert B. "U.S. Plans to Sell Atom Fuel Plants," *New York Times,* November 11, 1969, 1.

46. "Uranium Policy to Reap Major Revenue," *New York Times,* December 21, 1969, F13.

47. Sheppard, Jr., Nathaniel, "Uranium Shipments Banned by Chicago," *New York Times,* December 3, 1977, 11.

48. Holusha, John, "Fallout from Kyger Creek," *New York Times,* May 11, 1986, E5.

49. "$460 Million Emissions Project Planned at Power Plant," *Madison Courier,* May 12, 2006.

50. McElheny, Victor K. "A.E.C. Reports Accident at Uranium 235 Test Facility," *New York Times,* November 2, 1973, 17.

51. Franklin, Ben A., "Carter Pledge Kept on Atom Fuel Plant in Portsmouth, Ohio," *New York Times,* May 26, 1977, 15.

52. Hershey, Jr., Robert D., "U.S. to Shut Oak Ridge Atom Plant," *New York Times,* June 6, 1985, D1.

53. Ferguson II, Charles and Jack Boureston, "Laser Enrichment: Separation Anxiety," *Bulletin of Atomic Scientists,* March/April, 2005.

54. Charles, Dan. "U.S. Centrifuge Work Revived in Updated Form," *Washington Post,* April 23, 2007.

55. Wald, Matthew L., "U.S. Agrees in Landmark Accord to Cleanup of Nuclear Complex," *New York Times,* November 23, 1988, A1.

56. Kilborn, Peter T., "U.S. May Sell off Uranium Plants," *New York Times,* June 4, 1986, A1.

57. Wald, Matthew L., "In an Unusual Deal, U.S. will Sell Stock in its Uranium Mills," *New York Times,* June 30, 1998, A1.

58. Yggdrasil Institute: *Uranium Enrichment Newsletter*, May, 2000. Website of Earth Island Institute. (www.earthisland.org/yggdrasil/ UEN_may_2000.htm)

59. Film: *For My Working Life.* Produced by Karen Magid and Michael Grigsby. ATV Network Limited, 1980.

60. Malone, James and James R. Carroll, "U.S. Ignored Leukemia Concerns," *Louisville Courier-Journal,* September 5, 1999.

61. Alvarez, Robert, "The Risks of Making Nuclear Weapons: A Review of the Health and Mortality Experience of U.S. DOE Workers." Governmental Accountability Project. January , 2000. (www.downwinders.org/ DOE_worker_studies.htm)

62. Beyerlein and Hulsey, "Workers Fight for Compensation."

63. "Public Health Assessment: US DOE Portsmouth Gaseous Diffusion Plant, Piketon, Ohio." Agency for Toxic Substances and Drugs Registry. (www.atsdr.cdc.gov/HAC/PHA/portsmouthgas/pgd_p2.html)

64. "Public Health Assessment"

65. Malone, James, "Quest for Records Can Be Frustrating," *Louisville Courier-Journal,* June 27, 2000.

66. Hinchey, Frank, "Piketon Workers Share Their Stories," *Columbus Dispatch,* October 31, 1999.

67. "Worker Gets $100,000 from Uranium Plant," *Cleveland Plain Dealer,* Oct. 28, 1992, 5B.

68. Welsh-Huggins, Andrew, "NRC Suggests More Training at Plant," *Cleveland Plain Dealer,* November 1, 1999, 4B.

69. Ludlow, Randy, "Piketon Uranium Plant; Condensed Report Obscures Extent of Workers' Ills," *Columbus Dispatch,* July 24, 2005.

70. Ray.

71. Malone, James, "Nuclear Workers Exposed to Metal," *Louisville Courier-Journal,* February 5, 2004, 1A.

72. Bonfield, Tim, "Death Rates Elevated in Appalachian Areas," *Cincinnati Enquirer,* September 7, 1999, 1A. [Note: The title of this article was changed in the NewsBank index to "On mac, On mac," the meaning of which is not clear. The article is not listed at all in Newsdex: An Index to Local Newspaper Articles.]

73. Broad, William J., "Quietly, U.S. Converts Uranium into Fuel for Civilian Reactors," *New York Times,* June 19, 1995, A10.

74. Hebert, H. Josef, "U.S. Companies Complete Converting Weapons-Grade Uranium for Use in Power Plants," *Associated Press Worldstream,* July 13, 2006.

75. Wald, Matthew L., "U.S. Privatization Move Threatens Agreement to Buy Enriched Uranium from Russia," *New York Times,* August 5, 1998, A6.

76. Beyerlein, Tom and Lynn Hulsey, "Costly Centrifuge Plan Key to Piketon Revival," *Dayton Daily News,* November 14, 2006.

77. Wald, Matthew L., "Investors Not Told of Nuclear Plant Safety Issues, Group Says," *New York Times,* September 16, 1998, A14.

78. O'Neill, Tom, "Piketon Plant Closing: 'Lots and Lots of Unknowns,'" *Cincinnati Enquirer.* June 23, 2000, 1A.

79. Ludlow, Randy, "Piketon Tries to Cope with 'Devastating' Death," *Cincinnati Post,* June 23, 2000, 1A.

80. "USEC Selects Fluor as Engineer for American Centrifuge Uranium Enrichment Plant," *Business Wire,* June 21, 2004.

81. "USEC to Site American Centrifuge Plant in Piketon, Ohio; Technology Expected to Be World's Most Efficient for Enriching Nuclear Fuel," *Business Wire,* January 12, 2004, 5561.

82. Beyer, Clark and Jeff Combs, "Enrichment; Time for New Capacity." *Nuclear Engineering International,* September 12, 2005, 20.

83. "NRC Licenses New Enrichment Plant," *Electricity Daily,* June 28, 2006.

84. Beyer and Combs.

85. Snell, Marilyn Berlin, "Dangerous Liaisons," *Sierra Magazine* (May, 2005). (www.sierra club.org/sierra/200505/proliferation/printable_all.asp)

86. Hulsey and Beyerlein, "Piketon: A Troubled Past."

87. Radioactive Waste Management 172.

88. Hulsey and Beyerlein, "Piketon: A Troubled Past."

89. Rose, Van, "Plant Cylinders May Hold Toxic Phosgene Gas," *Pike County News Watchman,* October 26, 2005.

90. Yggdrasil Institute: *Uranium Enrichment Newsletter,* July, 2000. (www.earth island.org/yggdrasil/uen_jul2000.htm)

91. Hulsey, Lynn and Tom Beyerlein. "Groups Fear Piketon Will Become Dumping Ground." *Dayton Daily News,* November 14, 2006.

92. "Libyan Nuclear Material Airlifted to US and Russia," *Nuclear World Review,* March 12, 2004.

93. "USEC Drops Dividend, Buys Off Timbers," *Electricity Daily,* February 10, 2006.

94. Dizard, John, "Cracks Visible in a Power Monopoly," *Financial Times* (London, England) June 12, 2006, 7.

95. "Cleanup Chronology."

96. Knapik, Michael, "USEC Faces Prospects of Duties on Russian SWU," *Nuclear Fuel,* May 8, 2006, 1.

97. Wald, Matthew L., "Sole U.S. Company That Enriches Uranium is Struggling to Stay in Business," *New York Times,* June 12, 2007.

98. "USEC Spent $1.8 M Lobbying in 2007," *Associated Press,* August 15, 2007.

99. "Stupak, Dingell, Applaud Energy Department Decision to Reject $9.5 Billion Sole Source Contract Proposal for Energy Solutions and USEC," *States News Service,* October 2, 2007.

100. Wasserman, Harvey. "Anti-Nuclear Renaissance: A Powerful but Partial and Tentative Victory over Atomic Energy." Common Dreams News Center, January 5, 2008. (http://commondreams.org/archive/2008/01/05/6191/)

101. Beyerlein and Halsey, "Costly Centrifuge."

102. MacLachlan, Ann and Daniel Horner, "Areva Plans to Build U.S. Enrichment Plant, Cites Shortfall in SWU Capacity," *Nuclear Fuel,* 32 (July 2, 2007), 1.

103. Whitford, David, "America's Nuclear Revival," *Fortune,* April 1, 2007. Reprinted *CNNMoney.com.*

104. Makhijani, Arjun. "France's Nuclear Fix?" *Science for Democratic Action,* 15 (January, 2008), 5-8.

105. "Nuclear Waste Concerns Resurface." *Associated Press,* January 20, 2008.

106. Sea, Geoffrey. "A Brief Chronology."

107. Stolz, Martin and Matthew L. Wald, "Interior Department Rejects Interim Plan for Nuclear Waste," *New York Times,* September 9, 2006.

108. "Review of the SONIC Proposal to Dump High-Level Nuclear Waste at Piketon." Website of SONG (Southern Ohio Neighbors Group.) (http://ohioneighbors.org/SONIC.aspx) Also personal interview with Kathleen Boutis, January 19, 2008.

109. Ludlow, Randy, "Nuke-Rod Recycling Proposed," *Columbus Dispatch,* October 18, 2006, 35.

110. Hulsey and Beyerlein, "Groups Fear Piketon."

111. Why a FACA?" Fact sheet of SONG. (http://ohioneighbors.org/SONIC.aspx)

112. Beyerlein and Hulsey. "Workers Fight for Compensation."

113. Wehrman, Jessica, "Senators Upset Over Compensation Law," *Dayton Daily News,* July 5, 2007, A5.

114. "Weapons Plant Neighbors Can Sue: Health Threats Linked to Toxins," *Cincinnati Post* (August 27, 2007), A3

THE URANIUM LEAK: FEED MATERIALS PRODUCTION CENTER, FERNALD OHIO

Cincinnati is usually known as a conservative city, but its history is rather complex. The early days of the city were shaped by its presence on the Ohio River (the word "Ohio" comes from the Iroquois and means "great river"). During the steamboat days of the 1840s and 1850s it became a leading city in the country's development. Large numbers of German, Jewish, and Irish immigrants later established schools, libraries and cultural centers. When railroads replaced steamboats, Cincinnati continued to be a transportation center, and in the early 20th century developed diversified business and machine tool industries. African-Americans from the south and whites from Appalachia joined the workforce. In the mid-20th century Cincinnatian Robert A. Taft, the most powerful Republican conservative in the Senate, developed far-reaching anti-union legislation. His grandson and namesake was Ohio governor from 2000-2006.

In the spring of 1951 the Atomic Energy Commission announced its plans to locate a new atomic plant on one of the richest pieces of farmland in the area. The site was near the tiny town of Fernald Station, eighteen miles northwest of Cincinnati, 8/10 of a mile from the Great Miami River which replenishes the Great Miami Aquifer, a major water source for southern Ohio. Governor Frank

Lausche and Sen. John Bricker lobbied hard to bring the plant to Cincinnati; Fernald was chosen over 62 other sites. (1) As said earlier, state and local politicians regarded the acquisition of the plant as a plum, a sign that Cincinnati was going to be a leader in the new atomic age. The plant was also welcomed by the construction industry. (The first estimate was that the plant would cost $30 million to build, but it ended up costing four times that much). Apparently few at the time considered the possibility that locating a uranium plant near a major city with half a million people might be a mistake.

Residents in the Fernald area were not enthusiastic about the coming of the plant. Some of the farms had been in the same families for almost 200 years. The area was known, according to one resident, as the "sugar corn capital of the nation"; there were dairy farms (providing the milk for French Bauer dairies in Cincinnati) and farms for hogs and cattle. (2) Farmers were stunned by the government's announcement; they had already planned crops and field rotations. One said, "What is this? How can they take our farm when we don't want to sell?" (3) It's possible farmers near the other nuclear sites expressed similar anger about the army takeover of their land--they did so strongly when Jefferson Proving Ground was created, as we shall see--but, if they did, local papers did not acknowledge them.

The Army Corps of Engineers said they would offer residents a fair price for the land, and, if they refused, the courts would condemn the property so that it could be seized. (The concept of eminent domain meant the federal government could take what it wanted in the name of national security.) Residents had 30 days to accept the army offer. Three families in Harrison *did* refuse, and a few weeks later the government took their land. Though the families later tried to sue for compensation for the loss of their farms, they lost their court case, and were even given $38,000 less than originally offered to cover court costs. (4) A son of one of the farmers said: "Mom and Dad strove and worked hard from the depression of '32 to get what we had. We all cried like babies when they took our land." (5)

James F. Chandler of the Atomic Energy Commission assured the city that the plant would not damage the land.

> We've made tests of water, ground, air and vegetation, before construction started. When we have the plant in operation, we're going to run constant checks to see that there's no change in conditions....Our disposal facilities

have been completely checked and coordinated with top anti-pollution authorities. (6)

Within a few years, however, the contamination had begun, and, when production stopped forty years later, the land was uninhabitable.

Bulldozers arrived May 19, 1951. The 1,050 acre-site--much smaller than Paducah and Piketon--was flattened so that it looked, alternatively, "like a mud hole or a dust bowl." The first stage of the construction took a year and a half. Nearly 3,000 construction workers came from Cincinnati and other places throughout the Midwest.(7) Many of the workers lived in trailer parks in the tiny town of Harrison, Ohio, near the Indiana border. In 1952 a fight broke out at the plant between carpenters and laborers about which group was responsible for dismantling some scaffolding, and the next day the carpenters' union walked out. What was extraordinary about the incident was the way the local papers covered it. Large headlines announced an "outbreak" at Fernald; police were sent in to quell the "rioting" and "mob action." (8) The treatment was typical of the anti-labor bias of news stories of the time, which gave support to the Taft-Hartley notion that the power of unions should be curtailed. Without the federal government's tight control over its workforce--including the right to conceal information from workers--the massive arms buildup could never have taken place.

By 1953 the plant was in production, 90% complete. It was big. At the center of the 1,050-acre site was a 136-acre production area, containing ten large complexes where most of the uranium work took place. A Pilot Plant contained prototypes of both chemical and metallurgical processing equipment; a sampling and storage plant (Plant# 1) sorted ores that came in; there were four chemical processing plants (Plants #2/3, #4, #7 and #8) and three metals production plants (Plants # 5, #6 and #9). All the structures were gray, block-like, impersonal, made of concrete, corrugated asbestos [sic] and steel. (9) A 250-acre buffer zone surrounded the buildings, separating the main part of the plant from its neighbors. To the north were forested wetlands. A small stream, Paddy's Run, ran parallel to the western edge of the property. Open fields surrounding the plant were eventually leased for the grazing of cattle.

The first operator of the plant was National Lead of Ohio. (National Lead had once made the notoriously toxic Dutch Boy Lead Paint and at the time had no other uranium operations, though extensive experience in chemicals.) The first manager of the plant, George W. Wunder, was a native Cincinnatian. Early news stories about the purpose of the plant were somewhat vague. It produced "feed" uranium compounds and metals for other nuclear plants. The word "feed" was to cause confusion in the years ahead, perhaps intentionally. Some farm people in the area seeing the sign "Feed Materials Production Center" assumed the plant had something to do with agriculture. Its tower, painted red and white, making it look like the Purina checkerboard, only increased the misperceptions.

Most workers, too, were evidently kept in the dark about the precise purpose of the work. All of the ten complexes in the production area were interrelated in some way, but workers were not allowed to go from one part of the plant to another. "You couldn't wander all over the plant," said Greg Bassitt. "You had to stay in your plant where you were working, so you didn't know what went on in other plants." One woman said, "I did know some of the process, but I didn't know right away that our end product was being used for weapons....I knew that we were working for the government, and I knew it was classified, so I figured it wasn't for me to know everything." Workers were told never to talk about the operations of the plant; if people asked, they were to reply, "I'm not at liberty to say." (10)

ii

In 1955 a reporter for the *Cincinnati Post,* however, did get an exclusive tour of the plant and wrote a front page story: "Inside Fernald: Secrecy Lifted." His story emphasized how clean and safe the plant was (the story was written with the approval of the Atomic Energy Commission): the whole plant was "sterile as a hospital." One function of the plant was to take in raw uranium ore from all over the world. It arrived in chunks like coal; the uranium was the "black streaks" in the chunks. This ore was dried, ground and separated, then refined by chemicals to produce UO_3 (uranium trioxide). It then went through furnaces to produce UF_4 (uranium tetrafluoride), known as green salt because of its color. Initially this green salt was sent as "feed" to Paducah for enrichment in the gaseous diffusion process (11), but in 1956 Paducah constructed its own conversion facility. (12) Most of the materials at Fernald were converted into high purity uranium products in Plant #4. Materials were put into metal-lined containers which were then heated, cooled and broken open. The resulting uranium metal looked something like biscuits; eventually the forms were called "derbies" because of their resemblance to the hat. Derbies were then put into a graphite crucible and melted, the molten uranium spilling out into molds where it solidified as ingots. These pure uranium ingots were sent to Reactive Metals, Inc. in Ashtabula, Ohio, where they were heated and extruded using high pressure extrusion presses, then eventually sent on to Hanford and Savannah River, where they were used in the reactors which produced plutonium for bombs. (13)

The *Post* article said the uranium shipped out of Fernald in the 1950s was safe because it was only mildly radioactive. Yet what *was* dangerous--even the *Post* story said this--was the residue from the chemical processing, which was *highly* radioactive. According to the article, the waste was being stored temporarily in "underground" silos, until the countries which sold the United States the ore could "come and get it." These "temporary" concrete structures, known as Silo 1 and Silo 2, contained waste residue from Fernald and other plants. (The silos were sometimes called K-65 because they also contained the waste material from the K-65 plant at Oak Ridge where the Hiroshima bomb had been made. The buildings at Oak Ridge were labeled K; at Paducah, C; and at Piketon, X). This K-65 waste was legally "owned" by Belgium. In 1982 the U.S. bought the waste from Belgium, saying that it might want to extract the radium from it for resale, though this turned out not to be possible. (14) Another view is that the US agreed to keep the waste at Fernald in exchange for Belgium allowing the U.S. to put Pershing II and cruise missiles on their soil. (15) Over the years the uranium in the silos began to decay into radium, which then produced extremely dangerous levels of radon gas, which can be carried by the wind and is carcinogenic if inhaled. The silos eventually came to be seen as the most dangerous sites on the property.

The pressure on Fernald to produce in the 1950s was intense. Anticommunist fervor was high. One worker said he was convinced the Russians were "trying to whup us."(16) National Lead of Ohio drove the workers hard and never missed a production deadline. At the height of the bomb fever in the early 1960s the plant had nearly 3,000 employees. Workers said they sometimes had to work double shifts, 16 or 18 hours a day; they had no weekends off, no holidays. (17) In 2006 a retired supervisor said that National Lead had hired "goons" to bully them into working harder and keeping quiet about what they saw inside the compound. (18) In June, 1959 the *Cincinnati Enquirer* reported a wildcat strike of machinists, steelworkers and sheet metal workers, who refused to cooperate any longer with the quota system, though the story doesn't explain what the quota system was or why the workers were striking. (19) Occasionally there were news stories about accidents and fatalities. In March, 1954 two men died from burns in a chemical explosion (there were no radioactive materials involved, the plant said). (20) Residents who lived near the plant said they became accustomed to hearing alarms going off, and would say to one another, when they heard an alarm, "I wonder what blew up at the plant this time." (21) In 1958 a small plane crashed into the plant's inner fence. Though it presumably caused no serious damage, the pilot was grilled for five hours because he had flown over a restricted area. Later Fernald would not be subject to air space restrictions, but the vulnerability of all the nuclear sites has become an issue again since 9/11. (22)

iii

For the next 25 years few in Cincinnati paid much attention to Fernald. With the decline in bomb production in the 1960s, employment at the facility fell off, dwindling to less than a thousand. From 1960-1970 there were only 12 stories in the local papers about Fernald (in contrast to the 1,118 which appeared between 1985 and 1989 when the --metaphoric--lid blew off). Yet during this unreported period, significant things were happening.

For one thing, Fernald had secretly become the only thorium repository in the country. Because thorium is three times as plentiful as uranium on the earth's surface, the military believed it might eventually replace uranium and plutonium in the making of nuclear bombs. From 1954-1956 thorium was produced in Plant #9. In the 1960s Fernald purified thorium "feed" for Hanford's thorium oxide program, and in the late 1970s Hanford began to *return* thorium nitrate to Fernald, where it was converted into thoria gel and stored. (23) Thorium, however, like uranium, is both very toxic and very radioactive. Like uranium it decays into Radium-228, which can be nearly as lethal as plutonium. In the 1980s an *Enquirer* story revealed there were 2.4 million pounds of thorium compounds sealed in drums, and 11.8 million pounds buried in the unlined pits. (24) In 1990 thorium was found in Silo 3, leaking radon gas. Unlike Silos 1 and 2, which were filled with sludge, Silo 3 was filled with dry metallic ash and thought up to that time to be "cold." Radium was also found in Paddy's Run, which ran through the plant and into the Great Miami River. (25) Thorium has a half-life of 14 billion years.

Also in the 1960s Fernald began to use reprocessed uranium from the reactors at Hanford and Savannah River, rather than raw ore, to make the metal ingots. Some of this reprocessed uranium was contaminated with transuranic elements--including plutonium. As at Paducah and Piketon, the workers were not told about the danger or protected from it. In 1986 *Enquirer* reporter Anne Brataas wrote that the DOE had not required Fernald to maintain accountability records of the transuranics, and thus it could not be determined how much plutonium had actually been at the plant. The DOE guess was 50 grams (or 2 ounces) over 25 years. A local UC biology professor, however, pointed out that, if the uranium had not been sampled regularly, there was no way to determine the accuracy of the numbers. (26) The DOE assured the city of Cincinnati that the amount of plutonium was minimal and posed no threat, even though union consultants warned there was no safe level for plutonium and that even microscopic amounts can be fatal.(27)

In the 1970s Fernald also began to use depleted uranium for their metal fabrications. As a heavy metal U-238 (depleted uranium) is extremely hard. Thousands of barrels of U-238 were rusting at Oak Ridge, Paducah and Piketon, the refuse from the enrichment process. The DOE decided to use this depleted uranium to fabricate fuel rods for the reactors at Hanford and Savannah River. (28) This DU may also have been contaminated. In fact, Fernald officials admitted that in 1980 the plant had received a shipment from Paducah of 51,000 pounds of depleted uranium hexafluoride which had not one or ten parts plutonium per billion--which was considered acceptable--but almost 267 parts per billion. NLO said they had not wanted to process the material, but were "ordered to" by the DOE. "They wanted us to take the stuff because the containers it was in were leaking and they wanted to get rid of it. We never wanted to take it." Weldon Adams, assistant plant manager then, said it was "about the worst stuff we ever got in here." (29) The uranium was processed two years later by blending it with other materials to lower its radiation level, but workers again had not been protected against exposure. Only warning signs had been posted. (30)

In the 1970s the army gave Fernald a contract to research ways to use depleted uranium for penetrators for anti-tank weapons. (31) Though Fernald did the initial research on these projectiles, it didn't get the contract to make them. ERDA (the Energy Research and Development Agency, which had replaced the old Atomic Energy Commission and would later become the Department of Energy) was publicly saying then that all of the government nuclear plants were now only processing uranium for civilian nuclear power plants; they were no longer involved in war work. Pentagon contracts, ERDA said, went to private business. Yet one of the "private" companies which did get a contract to make the DU projectiles was a subsidiary of NL Industries in Colonie, New York--NL, of course, being the parent company of National Lead of Ohio, the operator of Fernald. The NL Colonie plant fabricated the projectiles until 1984 when it was closed because of contamination in surrounding neighborhoods. In one month it had released more radioactive material than permitted for the whole year. (32)

In February, 1986, Fernald again received some contaminated material from Paducah, but this time went public about it. Officials announced the DOE had authorized them to convert 168 tons of contaminated uranium powder from Paducah into metal, and to process 78,000 gallons of liquid waste containing plutonium. This time the plant said it planned to use protective suits and respirators and train workers in safety measures. (33) A few months later, though, Dan Arthur, the man hired to train the workers in safety procedures, quit because he felt the job was being rushed. (34) His concerns may have been justified, for two years later a "suspicious" liquid found in eleven barrels of "mismarked" waste turned out to contain plutonium, and thirty-five employees were exposed. Four workers had to be sent to the Battelle Laboratory in Hanford, Washington for whole body counts, though the tests turned out negative. (35)

When the *Washington Post* stories about the 12 ounces of plutonium at Paducah appeared in 1999, the *Enquirer* presented as fact that only 50 grams (2 ounces) of plutonium had been present from 1951 to 1989 at Fernald (though the story in 1985 had said this was only a conjecture, because the DOE had no hard data). By this time the remediation of Fernald was going on, and plant officials assured workers and residents that the plutonium, which had been put in the underground waste pits, had been excavated with the other wastes and shipped to Utah, and that the rest of the plutonium had "probably" been recycled into nuclear reactors and shipped out. (36) Whether a millionth of a gram of plutonium ever got into any anyone's lungs over the years at this point can never be known. By 1999 most of the scientists coming to Fernald were saying that the gravest danger facing the community was not from the plutonium, but from all the uranium.

iv

Initially workers had been told that uranium was not highly radioactive and would be safe to work with. Externally it is not dangerous, but if it gets inside the body it can be carcinogenic and damage cells. For years there had been emissions of gaseous uranium dust both inside and outside the plant, which the workers and nearby residents had inhaled. As early as 1959 government officials were aware that the dust collection bags ruptured almost once a month, releasing dangerous amounts of uranium particles into the atmosphere, but they did nothing about it. (37) Releases may also have been due to badly designed equipment, accidents, or negligence. A particularly bad accident occurred on Valentine's Day, 1966--the workers called it Black Monday--when a faulty valve released 4,000 pounds of uranium hexafluoride. White clouds filled the plant, causing a few workers to be hospitalized. (38) All of these atmospheric emissions were not only dangerous to the workers and residents, but as the heavy uranium particles fell on the land and water, the area itself became contaminated. By the time Fernald closed, it was estimated that over a *million* pounds of uranium had been released; some scientists feel the figure could be twice that high, a staggering amount. (39) A Center for Disease Control study in the late 1990s revealed that airborne particles carried by the wind had been discovered in soil and water over an area of eleven square miles. (40)

Though it was not until 1984 that the dangers of Fernald became public, in the years just before that time there were signs that people were becoming alarmed. For one thing, by the late 1960s workers and residents had, once again, begun to notice cancer clusters. A worker named Donald Wilson, his hands eaten raw by chemicals and his body covered with tumors, died of a rare form of cancer in 1962. He was 37. (41) Unions noticed a large number of lung cancers among workers, but were told by NLO that, if the workers "raised hell," the plant would shut down. (42) A nearby resident named Edwa Yocum began to keep a map with pins in it locating all the cancers she heard about in the five mile area of the plant. In 1990 there were 150 pins;(43) by 2003 there were 517: black for those dead, orange for those living with cancer. Many pins were in the area northeast (the wind direction) of the plant. (44) Another resident, Doris Clawson, kept a single sheet of paper on which she listed the cancers of her neighbors one after another. (45)

In 1980 a local environmental group called CARE (Citizens Against a Radioactive Environment) held a teach-in at the University of Cincinnati, focusing on the fact that water from Fernald was going into the Great Miami River and from there the Ohio, 24 miles downstream. A private lab in California had run a test for the group on some water from Paddy's Run, which had shown uranium twice the accepted level. (46) In 1983 some residents in the Branch Hill Mobile Home Park, a half mile from the plant, asked the DOE to test their well water. (47) The peace community in Cincinnati also became more demonstrative, since Reagan was installing first-strike nuclear weapons throughout the world and making veiled nuclear threats. In 1983 non-violent peace vigils began to be held at the gates of Fernald, where several activists were arrested and jailed. (48)

v

What brought the whole dangerous history of Fernald to light was a single incident in the fall of 1984 in Plant #9. The exhaust stream of the plant went through a series of large fabric bags which supposedly filtered out the uranium particles so they didn't escape into the atmosphere. In September, 1984 one of the fifty-two bags ruptured and uranium escaped. Plant officials didn't do anything about the bag at first because "it looked all right;" they thought the monitoring equipment, which signaled a problem, was malfunctioning. For the next two months over 350 pounds of uranium dust escaped. When the plant finally discovered the leak, they corrected the problem and notified Oak Ridge. On December 7, 1984 NLO shut down the dust collection system of Plant #9, and cautiously notified the press. NLO minimized the accident: there was no danger, the uranium was only mildly radioactive, all of the dust was contained on site. A few days later, however, both Cincinnati papers began to raise questions about the uranium releases at Fernald and to investigate the plant's other operations.

The DOE sent three experts to Cincinnati from their Oak Ridge office to allay the fears of residents about the leak. They had no idea what was awaiting them. At the public meeting one Thursday night at the Crosby Township Elementary School hundreds of people, workers and nearby residents, crowded into the auditorium; their fear, anger and frustration all came out. One local businessman said: "Why didn't you people monitor things better? That's what you're paid for. Where's your safety standards? You didn't have any!"(49) The meeting lasted three hours. One result was that the Oak Ridge officials finally agreed to let NIOSH conduct a health study of the workers (what the unions had been seeking for years). Also 150 people signed a sheet to discuss forming a local citizens' group. That night was the beginning of FRESH (the Fernald Residents for Environmental Safety and Health). A month later DOE officials announced that in 1981 and 1982 they had secretly tested three wells in the community *outside the plant* for uranium contamination and found that each had more than 36 times the safety levels. (50) Unfortunately for the DOE, one of the wells belonged to Ken and Lisa Crawford. When uranium was discovered in her well, Lisa Crawford said, "The mother instinct kicked in and I became one very angry person. Very angry." (51) For the next 20 years she was to be the president and the strongest voice in FRESH--and, in effect, the whole city--constantly confronting and challenging DOE assertions about the contamination at Fernald from the standpoint of community safety and health.

At the end of December, 1984 National Lead of Ohio decided not to bid for another five-year contract (citing its reason for leaving as "bad publicity"). For the next five years--until the plant finally closed--Fernald *was* in the public spotlight. Stories were in the papers every week, if not sometimes every day. Every new leak, accident or explosion was reported and analyzed; old accidents and uranium releases were exposed and explained. According to the *Enquirer,* there were "over a billion pounds of nuclear age garbage" at Fernald; only Hanford and Savannah River had more. (52) The state of Ohio fined Fernald for environmental violations and initiated a law suit. (53) Some cancer studies which had been done on the workers (but long suppressed) were brought to light, showing elevated levels of pancreatic, stomach, and lung cancers. (54) Workers became more vocal, going on strike in 1985 for the first time in 16 years, demanding that the plant lower levels of radiation exposure (NLO refused, saying all government plants had the same levels). (55) FRESH members repeatedly tried to get information from the federal government about the extent of the area contamination, but were always turned away. Finally, Cincinnati attorney Stanley Chesley filed a class action lawsuit on behalf of FRESH and the neighbors of Fernald for $300 million, citing pollution of the local environment, reduced property values and emotional stress. The connection between the emissions and cancer or other illnesses could not be proven definitively then, as all sides knew. (56) The lawsuit enabled independent scientific investigators to come in and assess the reliability of government documents and data about plant operations and uranium releases, and to point out ways that data may have been distorted or misused. Investigations were also done by the Ohio EPA, the General Accounting Office in Washington, a congressional subcommittee headed by Rep. Tom Luken of Cincinnati, and the Radioactive Waste Campaign of the Sierra Club. In 1990 the workers filed a class action lawsuit as well. By the end of the decade the Clawsons (multiple cancers in the family) had been on the cover of *Time* (October 31, 1988); Phil Donahue had filmed a community forum at nearby Hamilton High School; a FRESH meeting had been filmed as part of the CBS program *48 Hours;* and news reporters and camera men had come to Fernald from all over the world. (57). During Al Gore's 2000 presidential campaign, he made a special trip, while in Ohio, to meet Lisa Crawford. (58)

In 1986 Westinghouse assumed management of the plant. It made some upgrades to reduce emissions, and instituted quality control measures, but accidents at the plant continued. On January 19, 1986 an alarm failed to detect a split in a reactor which could have released a toxic chemical cloud, though an employee discovered the problem in time. In the next few months there were stories of leaks of radon gas out of the silos, leaks of plutonium-contaminated uranium from the T-hopper, and unauthorized burning of waste in the incinerator. (59) Rumors began the plant might close. The Secretary of Energy had said that the country was "awash in plutonium." Fernald had also lost its biggest "customer" for ingots when the N-Reactor at Hanford shut down in 1986 (for among other things, the similarity of its design to the reactor at Chernobyl). (60)

Westinghouse and the DOE began to go to FRESH meetings with charts, diagrams, slides and statistics, but residents said they left still wondering if the assurances they had been given were true, or whether they had just been "coddled with clichés and half-truths" about the health effects of low-level radiation. (61) In the meantime people in the area were still dying. Robert Alvarez of the Environmental Policy Institute reported that two studies of Fernald workers had shown increased death risks for all workers, as well as a significant risk for lung cancer. (62) The *Post* carried the story of the Charles and Linda Zinser family who had rented an acre of land 1½ miles from the plant near the Great Miami River. One two-year-old son was diagnosed with a rare form of bone cancer and had to have a leg amputated; their 8-year-old son was diagnosed with acute leukemia. Westinghouse denied that water from the plant could have contaminated the garden and caused the cancers (a UC environmental professor said the same thing), but a UC hematologist admitted that two rare cancers in one family was "suspicious." (63) A few years later elevated uranium levels were found in the milk of cows on nearby farms, and in a testing control farm 20 miles southwest of Fernald in Indiana. (64)

The residents' class action lawsuit against NLO was settled out of court for $78 million. Most of the settlement went to pay for long-term medical monitoring of the 14,000 residents and for community health studies; individuals themselves received only a few hundred dollars. As part of the agreement, the DOE said that *it* was responsible for all the problems at Fernald, not NLO, for NLO had notified them of safety problems at the plant, but the AEC and DOE had refused to correct them.(65) Though it is true that the AEC and DOE had always been notoriously unconcerned about worker safety, some in Congress believed the DOE's willingness to accept full blame for Fernald was also because it wanted to get NLO off the financial hook. A recent court decision (Boyle vs. United Technologies) had given government contractors immunity from liability if they had been operating "poorly designed equipment." (66) As we have seen in the stories of the other sites, the government's financial protection of the nuclear industry has been essential; it is the only reason these risky plants have continued to be built; they cannot get insurance otherwise. Thus the $78 million Fernald settlement came from the DOE (and taxpayers), not National Lead of Ohio. In 1988 workers went on strike again, because Westinghouse wanted to increase the cost of their medical insurance. (67) In 1994 the class action suit of the workers was settled for $20 million, the first legal victory for any group of nuclear workers. The settlement granted workers free annual medical check-ups for life, though some refused to take them, they said, out of fear of what they might learn. (68)

vi

Fernald was officially closed December 11, 1988 as part of Plan 2010, the Reagan White House "reconceptualization" of its nuclear program. Rocky Flats was to be closed at that time as well (there were fears that waste from its pluto-nium production was affecting Denver's water supply). Though two smaller nuclear facilities were also to be shut down, new reactors were also going up at Savannah River and Idaho Falls, so the production of radioactive materials--and radioactive waste--was going to continue. (69) Lisa Crawford expressed fear that the government would just "close up the gates and run," but it didn't, and that it didn't is a credit to her and the other residents who knew how important it was to continue monitoring government actions. (70) In 1989 Fernald was placed on the National Priorities List, eligible for Superfund status. In 1991 production finally ended. In 1992 the Fernald Environmental Restoration Man-agement Corporation (FERMCO) assumed responsibility for the cleanup. (Westinghouse did not re-bid; according to a later story, it was blamed for wast-ing $31 *billion* in tax money over a six year period). (71) FERMCO was the creation of another familiar nuclear player, the Fluor Corporation. FERMCO established its own local environmental restoration company--the first of its kind-- which was later known as Fluor Daniel Fernald and later simply Fluor Fernald.

The challenges of remediating Fernald were great. Officials in DOE's Envi-ronmental Management program--set up to deal with the contamination at all the nuclear production sites--were entering a new untested field. The contami-nated land could never be returned to its original condition, and since radioac-tive waste cannot be "cleaned up" or made less radioactive, its hazards can only be "contained" in some way, so that, as much as possible, the public and natural resources are protected from further contamination. One of the primary fears of the residents of Cincinnati was that the water supply of the city might be endan-gered. According to *Danger Lurks Below,* as much as 82 metric tons of radio-active wastewater had been dumped into the Great Miami River each day dur-ing the time of the plant's operation by way of a buried pipeline from the plant. (72) (Mound had also used the river for radioactive dumping, as much as 600,000 gallons of wastewater a day.) (73) For years the official government position was that putting the uranium in the river made it "safe," "diluted" it, even though radionuclides are not "dissolved" but continue to be radioactive, whatever the quantity of water. Because the Fernald plant sat on top of the

Great Miami Aquifer, there were concerns it might be contaminated either from waste water runoff from the plant or seepages from the radioactive substances in the waste pits. In 1990 it was confirmed there was a mile long plume of uranium in the southern part of the aquifer slowly moving southward towards the Ohio River (it was called the South Plume). At that time Fluor began to pump the contaminated water from the southernmost part of the aquifer to prevent the contamination from moving further south. At first the water was simply dumped back into the Great Miami River, but FRESH objected, saying that the water should be treated first. (Said Lisa Crawford, "Dilution is not the solution!") (74) A few years later extraction wells were constructed to the south of the plant, and millions of gallons of contaminated water *were* pumped from the aquifer and treated in the new Advanced Wastewater Treatment Facility (AWWTF). Unlike tritium and transuranic elements such as technetium, neptunium and plutonium, uranium *can* be extracted from water using present technology, though the process is slow. The Advanced Wastewater Treatment Facility at Fernald also treated contaminated storm water which ran off from retention basins during heavy rain. (75)

The remediation of Fernald was given high priority by the DOE, in part to counter the bad publicity of the 1980s, in part out of a desire to use the site as a laboratory to test out remediation methods and technologies. It also wanted to experiment working with "site-specific advisory boards." In 1992 the DOE created a Fernald Citizens Task Force--which later became the Fernald Citizens Advisory Board (CAB)--similar to other CABs at most of the former nuclear weapons sites. The Task Force was empowered to make recommendations to the DOE. (This group did not replace FRESH, which continued to meet, though Lisa Crawford and some other FRESH members became part of it.) Though much was made at the time of the new dialogue between government and citizens, in effect the DOE still had control of things: it was responsible for appointing people to the board and continued to shape the agenda. For instance, in 1988 when the announcement about the closure was made, a DOE official said the government would probably just clean up what it could and bury the rest. (76) This statement is almost identical to the recommendation made by the Task Force seven years later. The Task Force said the most dangerous highly radioactive materials should be excavated and shipped "elsewhere," but everything else would stay buried onsite. The chair of the Task Force said that reaching the final decision about keeping millions of tons of radioactive waste at Fernald was "very difficult" (it would still be right on top of the aquifer), but the DOE felt it would be too dangerous and expensive to truck all the contaminated soil and debris elsewhere.(77) Besides, where would it go? Who would take it? Lisa Crawford said, "It's not the perfect solution, but it's the best solution we're going to get....We're all going to have to bear part of the burden." (78) Once the DOE received the recommendation of the Task Force, it began to build an On-site Disposal Facility (OSDF) to treat and store the contaminated soil and debris.

vii

The most dangerous material onsite, everyone agreed, was what was in the six pits and the three silos; this is what the Task Force recommended be shipped elsewhere. As a temporary measure, in 1991 bentonite clay caps were put on the waste in the K-65 silos, which reduced the radon and gamma radiation levels for a time. Then Fluor decided to try a vitrification method to reduce the volume of waste at Fernald. According to this method, about 20,000 pounds of radioactive waste--uranium, thorium, other waste--would be melted into glass pellets. The pellets would still be radioactive, but would be immobile, not "leak," and thus could be stored, in relative safety, "somewhere out west." (79) $14 million was allotted for the vitrification process, but it ended up costing more than $69 million. And it was a colossal failure. Because it was behind schedule (and hurrying), Fluor evidently overlooked the warning of some employees that some of the pipes in the structure were made of substances which could melt if they came into contact with lead. When the test run was done December 26, 1996 this is what happened: a tube which was to help stir the waste was eaten away by lead in the waste, causing the molten mixture to leak out. (80) The General Accounting Office in Washington, appalled by the enormous cost overrun of the failed project, recommended that Fluor not be allowed to rebid for another contract (81), but the DOE refused to fire Fluor. Eventually Fluor decided to mix the waste into concrete blocks (which would be larger than the pellets, harder to transport, and, eventually, more apt to crumble in a shorter length of time), but it was afraid to try the vitrification again.

Originally there were fears that the cleanup of Fernald would cost $20 billion and take over 20 years, but when congressional budget-cutters in the 1990s were threatening cutbacks in cleanup funds, the DOE and Fluor decided to put Fernald on an Accelerated Cleanup schedule with the goal of bringing the site to EPA-approved radiation levels by 2010. Later Fluor was told, as were the remediators at Mound, that if it could meet the goal by 2006, it would receive a multi-million dollar bonus.

In 1995 Fluor hired International Technology Corporation to excavate the one million tons of waste in the pits--uranium, thorium, and other contaminants--treating it by thermal drying, so that it had the consistency of moist clumps of dirt. (The moistness was to prevent the waste from becoming powdery and susceptible to being carried off by the wind.) The waste was then put on railroad gondolas lined with heavy plastic, capped with metal tops, and shipped to the private disposal site, Envirocare in Clive, Utah. There were over 154 rail loads of pit waste in all; it was the largest rail transportation job in DOE history. (82) The last pit material arrived in Utah in June, 2005; four months later, however, some of the rail cars were still standing in rail yards in Ogden and Wendover because Envirocare was full. Though in 2004 Envirocare had received permission to double the size of its landfills, it had a backload of nuclear garbage from Oak Ridge and Rocky Flats as well as Fernald. (83)

Other radioactive waste from Fernald, from the debris of the dismantling of the buildings, was shipped by truck to the Nevada Test Site. In December, 1997 a white container of radioactive waste began to leak from a truck in Kingman, Arizona. For two years Fernald was forbidden to do any more truck shipping until changes in the containers and safety oversight were made. (84) In March, 2002 a truck from Fernald which was carrying two one-liter padded containers with a liquid solution of plutonium and neptunium [sic] was overturned by the wind on Interstate-80 outside of Laramie, Wyoming on its way to Idaho Falls. (85) There were no spills, but the issue of nuclear transport continued to raise fears.

Though the efforts to remediate the plant had strong community support, there were still many questions about the long-term health effects of the radiation exposure. In 1990 the National Cancer Institute had released a study of all the counties in which the country's 62 nuclear sites were located and concluded from their data that there was no evidence of increased cancer. Edwa Yocum, with her map, said simply, "I don't believe it." (86) The study was also later dismissed by medical experts, because of the questionable use and interpretation of data. In 2003 a long-term University of Cincinnati study of the Fernald residents was published, showing a prevalence of urinary system disease, elevations in bladder and kidney disease and chronic nephritis, as well as increased white blood cell count and hemoglobin levels.(87) The Fernald Medical Monitoring Program, begun as part of the lawsuit settlement, from which much of this medical data was drawn, is still going on and will finally come to an end in 2008. After that time researchers at the University of Cincinnati will make all the medical data assembled in the study available to other nuclear researchers. (88) A NIOSH study of the workers is also still going on; early findings in a mortality study showed high levels of lung and stomach cancer. (89) By the end of 2005, 1,148 former workers had applied for the $150,000 lump sum as part of the Energy Employees Occupational Illness Compensation. They were not eligible for the Special Cohort Status, as the Paducah and Piketon workers were, which meant they could not automatically apply for the compensation, but had to go through a slow dose-reconstruction study, sometimes based on spotty plant data, to see if they could prove that their radiation exposures were at least 50% responsible for their cancers. By December, 2005 over half of the claims had been rejected outright and only 192 approved. (90) One worker, who was approved, said, "We're getting guys turned down that were bombarded with all kinds of gases and fumes...because doctors and scientists say they don't meet the 50% criteria." (91) In February, 2007 the Advisory Board on Radiation and Worker Health of NIOSH held a three day public hearing, just north of Cincinnati, to hear once again the petitions of Mound and Fernald workers, or their survivors, who want all workers to have the "special cohort" designation, rather than have to do the cumbersome dose reconstruction, with often flawed or missing data. (92)

viii

The most difficult part of the remediation at Fernald was the unloading of the radioactive and chemical waste from the three silos. Silos 1 and 2 had radium-containing waste. Silo 1 also had waste products from the Mallinckrodt Chemical Works in St. Louis, a facility similar to Fernald; Silo 2 had waste from both Mallinckrodt and Fernald. (93) Fluor employed a complex, sophisticated engineering operation of computers and mechanical systems to excavate the silo waste. (94)

It was difficult, however, finding a place which was willing to take the silo waste once it was excavated. Initially the DOE wanted to send it all to Envirocare in Utah. Lobbyists for Envirocare (including the firm of the notorious Jack Abramoff) tried to get Congress to insert an amendment to the Energy bill, so that the Fernald waste could be reclassified as "byproduct ore," and thus get around Utah's environmental requirements. (95) The Utah legislature, however, did not want the "hot" silo material and refused to accept it. The DOE then tried to send it to the Nevada Test Site which was already receiving some of Fernald's waste. Nevada, however, didn't want the silo waste either, saying it wasn't licensed or set up to receive material this radioactive. The Nevada Attorney General threatened to sue to stop the Fernald shipment. A deputy attorney general said, "This material is singularly dangerous. I'm very sympathetic with the people of Ohio who want to get rid if it, but we're not the dumping ground for the whole country." (96)

In the spring of 2005, the DOE announced it had found a place for the waste from Silo 1 and Silo 2: Waste Control Specialists in the small town of Andrews, Texas (pop 10,000), not far from the Texas-New Mexico border. Though initially established as a site for hazardous waste only, it had become temporarily licensed to accept radioactive material due to the political manipulations of a Dallas billionaire named Harold Simmons, a Republican fund-raiser and supporter of then Governor George W. Bush. Simmons had made his fortune in lead in NL Industries, the old parent company of National Lead of Ohio, which had operated Fernald in the beginning--a connection which can hardly be a coincidence. The DOE paid Waste Control Specialists $75 million to take the waste from Silo 1 and 2, where it will be stored "temporarily" in steel tanks on a 10-acre asphalt pad. WCS is applying for a permanent storage license, but the decision will not come till mid-2008. Simmons has evidently been contributing millions to Texas legislators to get them to vote favorably for a permanent license. (97) It's possible that if WCS doesn't get a permanent license in two years, the dangerous waste from Fernald will have to move "somewhere" again. The Lone Star chapter of the Sierra Club is trying to stop the license. A geology researcher from Texas Tech says there are surface fractures in the red clay soil, and it's uncertain how deep they go. (98) Drs. Arjun and Annie Makhijani, who have studied the problems of the Fernald waste extensively over the years, say that there were "egregious errors" in the WCS license application, and that the Fernald waste, if left above-ground at Andrews, could have higher radiation levels as the material decays. Their studies indicate that a maximally exposed person in the future coming into contact with the waste could experience a dose 246 to 800 times higher than the present regulatory limit of 25 millirems per year. (The Drs. Mahhijani have been deeply critical of the "fast-track" cleanups at both Fernald and Rocky Flats, because "timetables were tied to bonuses without reference to radioactive doses to future generations.") (99)

The first shipment of the waste from Silos 1 and 2 left on its 1,300 mile journey to Texas on June 6, 2005. Each truck carried two containers, each weighing about 20,000 pounds; fifteen trucks were scheduled to leave each day. Though the local papers did not report any problems with the transport, other papers did, saying that, as of early July, only 15 shipments had arrived in Texas. Fluor had found some problems with the composition of the waste and was still trying to lessen the radiation levels. (100) By May, 2006, however, nearly all of the waste from Silos 1 and 2 had arrived at Andrews. (101)

The "dry" thorium-bearing waste in Silo 3, less radioactive than that in Silos 1 and 2, turned out to be more problematic than anticipated, and a $41 million waste extraction and packaging facility (involving robotics) had to be built to get the cement-like encrustations from the bottom. This waste left for Envirocare in Utah in April, 2006. (102) The Drs. Makhijani believe that, although this waste has been classified as Class A Low-Level Radioactive Waste, it contains Thorium-230, which will decay into Radium-226 in about 50 years, making it far more radioactive than what Envirocare presently allows (in fact about 10,000 times more radioactive). (103) Again, in the rush to meet the bonus deadline, studies about the future dangers of the waste were ignored.

ix

Though the dangerous waste from the three silos has been removed from Fernald, 85% of the waste which the facility generated is still there. The DOE has determined the waste is "low-level," but the phrase is misleading. "Low-level" does not mean the waste is not radioactive or potentially harmful; the phrase merely distinguishes it from "high level waste" from nuclear power plants. The low-level waste at Fernald--soil and debris contaminated with uranium, thorium and radium--is now buried in the On-Site Disposal Facility. The OSDF covers 123 acres and is divided into eight earthen mounds, called "cells," which resemble giant quonset huts. The clay bottoms of the cells were filled with a five-foot thick liner system--stones, fibers, plastics, as much material as possible--to make them impermeable. The radioactive waste was put in and covered with three feet of limestone rocks and six feet of other material. At the end of October, 2006, the last of the eight cells was filled. Eventually all the cells will be covered with earth so that the location resembles a giant hill. (104) The DOE has said that the OSDF has been designed to "remain stable a 1,000 years to the extent reasonable, and in any case no less than 200." The uncertainty of this language is not very reassuring; it shows the industry itself knows the technology of waste disposal is still experimental and untried. (105) The Drs. Makhijani have pointed out a serious systems error in the DOE computer program estimating "allowable residual radioactivity" in the Fernald cells, suggesting that some of the DOE data may already be flawed. (106) The DOE says that it will monitor the hill "in perpetuity," that is, forever--as long as there is a DOE and for that matter a United States. The Fernald waste will always be potentially hazardous. Uranium-235 has a half-life of 700 million years.

The other 900 acres of the site are presently being converted into a wildlife refuge of forest, prairies and wetlands which will be known as the Fernald Preserve. These acres are not suitable for agriculture or residences, but visitors will be able to walk through the refuge, which will be filled with a variety of plants, birds and animals. It's not known at this time if any contamination is already in the ecosystem. Back in the 1980s two Miami University zoologists found genetic malformation in some toads near the waste pits --the DOE dismissed this story (107)--and uranium *has* been found in wildlife at some of the other closed nuclear sites, but thus far there have been no reports of wildlife studies at Fernald. Most of the photographs of the wildlife refuge which have appeared in the papers so far look idyllic. Jim Homer, head of the restoration, said in July, 2006 that ideally visitors will have no idea the wetlands, plants and forest ecosystems were once a hazardous site (108)--which is no doubt the government's intention.

Some concern still exists about the radionuclides in the water. In January, 2004 the DOE proposed dismantling the Advanced Wastewater Treatment Facility, and simply dumping the wastewater directly into the river again, raising drainage limits 17 times the current levels. FRESH raised an outcry. Lisa Crawford said, "We don't want anything else dumped into the river. No, no, no. We have a binding agreement for the cleanup of the groundwater for the site." (109) The EPA objected to the plan as well, so the DOE decided instead to build a smaller wastewater treatment facility (¼ the size of the original) and to leave the discharge limits unchanged. (110) According to the *New York Times,* it will not be till 2023 that all the uranium is removed from the aquifer beneath Fernald. (111)

The total taxpayer cost of the Fernald clean-up will be about $4.4 billion. On January 22, 2007 the Department of Energy officially declared that Fluor had met all of its cleanup requirements (112), so the company received the millions of bonus dollars.

The Office of Legacy Management of the DOE replaced the Office of Environmental Management, and the S. M. Stoller Corporation was given the contact for the "surveillance, maintenance and technical support" of the site. (113) FRESH had its last (emotional) meeting in November, 2006. A new group, the Fernald Community Alliance, will ostensibly act as monitors, (114) but it is not clear to what extent the general public will be kept informed about the radiation levels, or any problems with the containment--for instance, should the cells begin to leak. As with the other nuclear sites, the story of Fernald is still a long long way from being over.

Notes: Fernald

1. *Fernald at Fifty: From Weapons to Wetlands.* (Ross, Ohio: Fluor Fernald Public Affairs Department, 2001), 4.

2. Film: *First Link: A Story of Fernald.* Fluor Fernald, 2001.

3. "News of $30,000,000 Uranium Plant Affects Workers Like A Bomb Blast," *Cincinnati Times-Star,* March 31, 1951, 1.

4. "Uncle Sam Gets Break: Jury Verdict Backfires on Landowners Seeking More for Fernald Plant," *Cincinnati Enquirer,* December 9, 1952, 1.

5. *Fernald at Fifty* 5.

6. "Fertile Fields Acres Soon to Produce Again, This Time for Freedom," *Cincinnati Post,* September 26, 1951, 24.

7. *First Link.*

8. "County Police are to Stand By in Fernald Outbreak," *Cincinnati Enquirer,* May 22, 1952, 1.

9. Cornell, Si, "Inside Fernald: Secrecy Lifted on Key to World's Future," *Cincinnati Post,,* December 15, 1955, 1.

10. *Fernald At Fifty* 8, 20.

11. Cornell 1.

12. *Fernald at Fifty* 12.

13. *Fernald at Fifty* 13, 11.

14. "U.S. Now Owns Nuclear Waste," *Cincinnati Post,* August 31, 1983, B6.

15. Coyle, D. and L. Finaldi, E. Greenfield, M. Hamilton, E. Hedemann, W. McDonnell, M. Resnikoff, J. Scarlott, and J. Tichenor, *Deadly Defense: Military Radioactive Landfills. A Citizen's Guide* (New York: Radioactive Waste Campaign, 1988), 118-119.

16. *First Link.*

17. *First Link.*

18. O'Farrell, Peggy, "Retired Supervisor Now Battles System," *Cincinnati Enquirer,* July 23, 2006.

19. "Strike Ends at Fernald Plant," *Cincinnati Enquirer,* June 29, 1959, 11.

20. "Second Fernald Plant Victim Dies," *Cincinnati Post,* March 20, 1954, 2.

21. *First Link.*

22. "No Fear of Flying over Fernald Site," *Cincinnati Enquirer,* March 28, 1989, A9.

23. *Fernald at Fifty* 9.

24. Brataas, Anne, "Fernald Stockpiles Thorium for Nation," *Cincinnati Enquirer,* April 20, 1986: A1.

25. Salvato, Al, "Thorium at Fernald," *Cincinnati Post,* August 30, 1990, 10A.

26. Brataas, Anne, "Fernald Radiation Danger Unclear," *Cincinnati Enquirer,* March 30, 1986, A16.

27. Brataas, Anne, "Leak: Can Fernald Handle Plutonium with Care?" *Cincinnati Enquirer,* March 30, 1986, A1.

28. *Fernald at Fifty* 17.

29. "Traces of Plutonium Found at Fernald Plant," *Cincinnati Post,* March 8, 1985, 1B.

30. "Plutonium Traces Worry Union at Fernald," *Cincinnati Enquirer,* March 9, 1985, D2.

31. "Firm Gets Army Bullet Contract," *Cincinnati Post,* April 21, 1977, 19.

32. "NLO Owner Shut Down Another Plant After Leaks," *Cincinnati Post,* January 12, 1985, 1B.

33. "Plutonium Safety Measures to be Reviewed," *Cincinnati Enquirer,* April 17, 1986, C1.

34. "Plutonium Project Begins," *Cincinnati Enquirer,* August 26, 1986, B3.

35. "Fear of Fernald Workers: 'The Unknown,'" *Cincinnati Post,* September 16, 1988, 1B.

36. Melcer, Rachel, "Fernald Off DOE Site List," *Cincinnati Enquirer,* September 25, 1999, 1C.

37. Noble, Kenneth B., "Risk to Thousands: Documents Indicate a Decision Not to Act on Major Cleanup," *New York Times,* October 15, 1988, 1.

38. "Fernald Haunted by Black Monday in 1966," *Cincinnati Enquirer,* February 26, 1989, B1.

39. Radioactive Waste Management Associates, *Danger Lurks Below: The Threat to Major Water Suppliers from the U.S. DOE Nuclear Weapons Plants.* Written for the Alliance for Nuclear Accountability, 30 (www.ananuclear.org)

40. "Contamination at the Fernald Site." Website of the Fernald Citizens Action Board. (http://www.feranldcaab.org/contamination.html)

41. Klepal, Dan, "Fernald Workers Fight for Payback," *Cincinnati Enquirer,* November 16, 2003: A1.

42. "Health Risks Found at Uranium Plant," *Cincinnati Post,* December 14, 1984, 1.

43. "Fernald Residents Mistrust Cancer Study," *Cincinnati Post,* September 20, 1990, 8A.

44. Sloat, Bill, "Health Fears Still Stalk Atom Plant's Neighbors," *Cleveland Plain Dealer,* November 13, 2003, A1.

45. "Plant's Neighbors Play Difficult Game," *Cincinnati Enquirer,* December 11, 1988, A11.

46. "Anti-Nuke Group Says EPA Ignoring Radiation in Creek," *Cincinnati Enquirer,* January 13, 1980, B7.

47. "Residents Seek Test on Water," *Cincinnati Post,* September 20, 1983, D1.

48. "Anti-Nuke Rally Ends with Arrest of Six Protestors," *Cincinnati Enquirer,* July 17, 1983, A1.

49. "Anger Vented," *Cincinnati Post,* December 14, 1984, 12B.

50. "High Uranium Levels Reported in Wells," *Cincinnati Post,* January 12, 1985, 1A.

51. *Fernald at Fifty* 20.

52. "Atomic Age Trash Pile is the Biggest Threat," *Cincinnati Enquirer,* December 11, 1988, A13.

53. "Ohio Will Sue Over Fernald Leaks," *Cincinnati Enquirer,* December 21, 1984, A1.

54. "Health Risks Found" 1.

55. "Limit Set on Radiation Exposures is Standard, NLO Workers Told," *Cincinnati Enquirer,* October 12, 1985, C5.

56. *Fernald at Fifty* 20.

57. *Fernald at Fifty* 20.

58. Melcer, Rachel, "Fernald Activist Hangs Tough," *Cincinnati Enquirer,* November 18, 1999, 1B.

59. "Fernald Optimism Meets Public Skepticism," *Cincinnati Enquirer,* May 18, 1986, A4.

60. D'Antonio Michael, *Atomic Harvest: Hanford and the Lethal Toll of American's Nuclear Arsenal* (New York: Crown, 1993), 131.

61. "Fernald Optimism" A4.

62. Alvarez, Robert, "Risks to Uranium Process Workers." Originally published in *British Medical Journal.* Available at "Projects: Institute for Policy Studies." (http://www.ips-dc.org/projects/nuclear/risksupw.htm)

63. "Acre of Heartaches," *Cincinnati Post,* June 28, 1986, 1B.

64. Miller, Nick "Sample Taken from Fernald's A-Bomb Waste," *Cincinnati Post,* October 26, 1990, 8A.

65. "Fernald Aid from DOE Uneven," *Cincinnati Enquirer,* October 9, 1988, B5.

66. Noble, "Risks to Thousands" 1.

67. Noble, Kenneth, "Amid Building, Fears Rise over Ohio Uranium Plant's Future," *New York Times,* November 26, 1988, 7.

68. "Fernald Settlement, A Mixed Blessing for Workers," *Cleveland Plain Dealer,* October 3, 1994, 5B.

69. "Fernald to Close," *Cincinnati Enquirer,* December 11, 1988, A1.

70. "Report Inspires More Worry," *Cincinnati Enquirer,* December 11, 1988, A1.

71. "Fernald Equipment Hot, Report Says $2.4 Million Worth Missing, GAO Finds," *Cleveland Plain Dealer,* June 6, 1994, 3B.

72. Radioactive Waste Management 28.

73. Radioactive Waste Management 103.

74. Holthaus, David, "Fernald to Dump Water," *Cincinnati Post,* November 15, 1990, 10A.

75. "Fernald Remediation." Report of the Fernald Citizens' Action Board. (www.fernaldcab.org/fernaldremed.html).

76. "'Clean What You Can and Bury What Is Left,'" *Cincinnati Enquirer,* December 11, 1988, A13.

77. Applegate, John, "Fernald (of all places) Offers a Model for Revitalizing Democracy." *Cincinnati Post,* November 21, 1995, 16A.

78. "U.S. Officials OK Plan to Dispose of Tainted Soil from Fernald," *Cleveland Plain Dealer,* February 9, 1996, 7B.

79. "Fernald Project to Convert Waste into Glass Beads," *Cleveland Plain Dealer,* August 1, 1993: 15B.

80. Wald, Matthew L., "Report Faults Energy Department on Managing Nuclear Site," *New York Times,* October 24, 1997, A27.

81. Gallagher, Mike and Tim Bonfield, "GAO on Fernald: Cleanup Botched; Millions Wasted," *Cincinnati Enquirer,* March 19, 1997, A1.

82. Klepal, Dan, "Dredging Done at Fernald Pits," *Cincinnati Enquirer,* June 16, 2005, 3C.

83. "Rail Cars Backing up with Waste for Envirocare Dump," *Associated Press State & Local Wire,* October 1, 2005.

84. Melcer, Rachel, "Waste Facing Roadblocks," *Cincinnati Enquirer,* April 30, 1999, 1B.

85. "No Radioactive Spill in Accident," *Cincinnati Post,* March 29, 2002, 15A.

86. "Fernald Residents Mistrust" 8A.

87. Pinney, Susan and Ronald Freyberg, Gail H. Levine, Donald E. Brannen, Lynn S. Mark, James M. Nasuta, Colleen D. Tebbe, Jeanette M. Buckholz and Robert Wones. "Health Effects in Community Residents Near a Uranium Plant at Fernald, Ohio, USA." *International Journal of Occupational Medicine and Environmental Health,* 16 (2003), 139-153.

88. Kinney, Terry, "UC Shares Fernald Radiation Data, *Cincinnati Post,* August 16, 2007, A2.

89. Yiin, James, "Cohort Mortality Study of Fernald Environmental Management Plant (FEMP)" NIOSH Occupational Work Program. (www.cdc.gov/niosh/oerp/ongoing.html)

90. "Claims Denied for Ex-Fernald Workers," *Cincinnati Post,* December 28, 2005, A11.

91. "Labor Department Rejects Most Claims from Uranium Plant Staff," *Associated Press State & Local Wire,* December 27, 2005.

92. O'Farrell, Peggy, "Fernald Workers, Families State Case," *Cincinnati Enquirer,* February 7, 2007, 1B.

93. Makhijani, Annie and Arjun Makhijani, "Shifting Radioactivity Risks: A Case Study of Waste Management at the Fernald Nuclear Weapons Site," *Science for Democratic Action,* 14 (November, 2006), 1. Also available at www.ieer.org/reports/fernald/.

94. Hansen, Brian, "Officials Say Fernald Silo Cleaned and Waste Shipped without Incident." *Inside Energy,* April 17, 2006, 6.

95. Fahys, Judy, "Rogue Lobbyist Had Ties to Utah," *Salt Lake Tribune,* January 12, 2006, A1.

96. Nolan, John, "Nevada Threatens Suit to Block Fernald Waste," *Cincinnati Post,* April 16, 2004, A18.

97. Wilder, Forrest, "Going Nuclear in West Texas," *Texas Observer,* February 18, 2005. (www.texasobserver.org); also "Toxic Texas Tour: WCS and Bush." Website of Texas Public Employees for Environmental Responsibility. (www.txpeer.org/toxictour/wcs.html).

98. Blaney, Betsy, "Town Embraces Radioactive Waste Storage, Disposal Industry," *Mount Vernon News,* April 30, 2005.

99. Makhijani 7.

100. Holland, Elizabethe, "Delays Slow Radioactive Shipments," *St. Louis Post Dispatch,* July 1, 2005, B1.

101. Cornwell, Lisa, "Last of Most Dangerous Waste at Former Uranium Plant Headed Out," *Associated Press State & Local Wire,* May 25, 2006.

102. O'Farrell, Peggy, "Fernald Cleanup Close to Finished," *Cincinnati Enquirer,* April 12, 2006, 2C.

103. Makhijani 10.

104. O'Farrell, Peggy, "Fernald Cleanup Update Tonight," *Cincinnati Enquirer,* September 27, 2006, B3.

105. DOE Environmental Management Website. (http://web.em.doe.gov/lfrg/fernald_facts.html)

106. Makhijani 12.

107. "Flora, Fauna at Fernald Scrutinized," *Cincinnati Enquirer,* March 10, 1989, A1.

108. O'Farrell, Peggy, "Wildlife Getting Comfortable Where Once Poison Ruled," *Cincinnati Enquirer,* July 23, 2006.

109. Sloat A1.

110. "Letter from the Fernald Citizens Advisory Board to Robert A. Warther, Department of Energy." (www.ananuclear.org/ohiolettermarch10,html)

111. Maag, Christopher, "Nuclear Site Nears End of Its Conversion to a Park," *New York Times,* September, 20, 2006.

112. "Fluor Receives Formal Acceptance from U.S. Department of Energy; Fernald Cleanup is Complete," *Business Wire,* January 29, 2007.

113. "Energy Department Awards Small Business Contract for Legacy Management Work to S. M. Stoller Corporation," Energy Department Documents and Publications, July 2, 2007.

114. Cornwell 2C.

Tritium In The Maple Trees: Maxey Flats Low-Level Radiation Waste Disposal, Maxey Flats, Kentucky

From the beginning of the nuclear age scientists were casual about the disposal of radioactive waste. J. Robert Oppenhemier at Los Alamos evidently dumped some of the waste from the Manhattan Project into canyons in New Mexico without thinking much about it. (1) Most early nuclear scientists were similarly unconcerned about the radioactive garbage which was accumulating, though they knew something eventually would have to be done. Glen Seaborg, the scientist who discovered plutonium and who later became one of the nuclear industry's strongest advocates, said--surprisingly--in 1955 that the fact that scientists had not figured out what to do with the waste might "limit" the extent to which atomic power was used in the future. (2) Unfortunately, he was wrong. The frenetic weapons buildup in the 1950s, then the development of nuclear power in the 1960s, created millions of tons of waste which no one knew what to do with. Scientists today have developed plans to try and contain the effects of some of this waste, but no one knows for sure how long these containment strategies will last or how effective they will be. Some of the waste will continue to be radioactive for billions of years.

In the early days the Atomic Energy Commission distinguished between two kinds of waste: high-level and low-level. High-level referred to nuclear fuel which had been used in nuclear power reactors and was "spent," that is, no longer effective in generating power. Spent fuel is very radioactive and thermally very hot, which means it has had to be kept in cooling ponds. Sludge from reprocessing (separating uranium and plutonium from other fissionable products--the process George W. Bush wants to revive, possibly at Paducah or Piketon) is also high-level waste. Some of this sludge has been solidified, but most is stored for the time being in underground tanks. No permanent repository for high-level waste has yet been found, and because so many geological questions have been raised about the proposed site at Yucca Mountain, it is uncertain at this time *where* it will all finally go. It is called high-level because it is extremely dangerous; direct exposure within a few minutes can be fatal, and it remains highly radioactive for hundreds of thousands of years.

Low-level waste was originally a kind of catch-all phrase for anything else which had been exposed to or was contaminated by radioactive material. The radioactivity of low-level waste could be very low (just above background radiation level) or quite high (such as that of plutonium and the other transuranic elements). Low-level did not mean it was not dangerous. Later the Nuclear Regulatory Commission made more careful distinctions between the different kinds of low-level waste. Transuranic elements such as plutonium were put in a separate category, as were uranium mill tailings from the processing of ores; mixed wastes which were both chemically hazardous and radioactive were also in a separate category. Today there are three categories of low-level waste: A, B and C, with C containing the greatest concentration of radionuclides. (There is also a category GTC, greater than C.) The letter designation is supposed to determine where and how the waste can be disposed of. Originally the private facility Envirocare (now Energy Solutions) in Utah was established to take in A level waste only, but its license has been modified so that it now allows B and C as well. WIPP in New Mexico was originally to be for the disposal only for plutonium and transuranic waste, but now it is also taking in high-level waste. Because of these regulatory changes, some of the distinctions between the kinds of waste are becoming blurred again. (3)

Much of the military's waste in the early years was simply dumped into the ocean. Barges regularly took 55-gallon drums lined with concrete and dumped them at sea, the three principal sites being two near Farollon Island, 50 miles from San Francisco, and one about 120 miles from the tip of New Jersey. This practice was not stopped by the Atomic Energy Commission until 1970. In 1976 an EPA oceanographer named Robert Dyer discovered that one-fourth of the Farollon Island containers had ruptured and that plutonium contaminants in the sediments were high. The radioactive contamination of fish and aquatic life has been a concern of oceanographers and environmentalists ever since. When the Atomic Energy Commission decided to stop dumping waste into the ocean, it was not because of concern about the environment--of which it had little--but because of the expense of the barge operations. (4)

In the 1950s low-level waste disposals existed at the weapons production sites at Hanford and Savannah River. In May, 1960 the AEC said that commercial radioactive waste--from hospitals, for instance, or industrial research--could temporarily be buried at Oak Ridge and Idaho Falls, along with military waste, until private low-level sites could be developed. In the late 1950s Kentucky governor Bert Combs and his economic advisors sought to locate one of these new private sites in eastern Kentucky. With the Paducah enrichment plant operating full-steam in western Kentucky, the politicians believed that Kentucky could become an important and wealthy player in the new atomic world. The AEC granted Kentucky a license for a low-level disposal site in Fleming County, in the heart of the bluegrass region, a largely rural area of dairy farms, tobacco fields and mineral springs. Kentucky was the second state granted a private nuclear waste license (Nevada was the first, for a site in Beatty). At first Governor Combs wanted the AEC to give the state "full control" over the waste site, saying, rather portentiously, that dual state/federal regulation would "seriously impair this nation's race with the Soviets to discover new and constructive applications of nuclear energy for the benefit of our citizens and the nation." (5) Though Combs didn't get his wish for complete freedom from federal regulation, it became evident in years ahead that AEC rules were lax, if not broken, at Maxey Flats. And the results were catastrophic.

ii

Three mistakes were made in the initial development and management of the site at Maxey Flats. The first was in the geological assessment of the location. Two different geological studies had been done to assess the appropriateness of the site for radioactive waste disposal. One was an academic study largely funded by the National Engineering Company (NECO) of Pleasanton, California, the same company which wanted to operate the site once it was built. (NECO had already bought land for the disposal site in Beatty, Nevada, which was to have a similarly disastrous history.) At Maxey Flats the geologists hired by NECO drilled wells, found them dry, and said they believed the shale was impermeable; their report said radioactive waste would not be able to migrate through the soil for centuries. A government group of geologists, however, some with the United States Geological Survey, had more reservations. They discovered some wells in the area filled up rather quickly, and concluded there might be fissures, fractures or hairline cracks in the shale, which meant that the groundwater flow could not be accurately predicted. Their doubts were overlooked. Kentucky was avid to get the disposal site and went with the report of the NECO business group. (6)

In 1962 NECO--secretly, according to some accounts--purchased 280 acres of land near the tiny town of Maxey Flats--65 miles east of Lexington, 10 miles north of Morehead, 17 miles west of Flemingsburg, the county seat. The land had once been a tobacco field; there were more than 120 wells and 25 springs within five miles of the location. The disposal site was located on a ridge 300 feet high which dropped steeply on three sides to the valley below. Through the valley ran Rock Lick Creek, a tributary of the Licking River which feeds into the Ohio. (7) NECO purchased the land, then sold it to the state of Kentucky, which granted it an operating license--another murky relationship between government and industry which would cause problems for the state years later. In 1962 construction began. According to resident Nancy Powell, the construction was fairly inconspicuous; not many in the region knew what was going on. (8) The Maxey Flats Low-Level Radiation Disposal Site officially opened in 1963. Like the other private sites being developed then--in Beatty, in Sheffield, Illinois, in West Valley, New York, in Richland, Washington, and in Barnwell, South Carolina--Maxey Flats came into being without much planning, guidance or supervision from the federal government. NECO seemingly followed the practices the federal government was using then to dispose of its waste at Hanford and Savannah River: it simply dumped the waste into trenches in the ground and covered it with dirt. These (unlined) trenches which held the waste were about 150 feet long, 70 feet wide and 30 feet deep. They were supposed to be covered by 10 feet of soil, but sometimes the coverage was only 6 feet, sometimes only six inches. Some of the waste was disposed of in wooden crates, cardboard boxes, paper bags, metal drums; some waste was simply put directly into the ground. (9) Nancy Powell said: "In the late 60s they would dig trenches and leave them open. They used the old kick-and-roll method--back a truck in and kick the stuff out. I used to see boxes and containers with that death's head on it." (10) Up to this time no independent monitoring had been done at any of the government nuclear disposal sites, so there was no evidence that they were not safe. (11)

It was the *nature* of the waste brought to Maxey Flats which caused the second major problem. Initially the site was supposed to take in medical garbage and low-level radioactive equipment from research labs, manufacturing companies, government and health care facilities: X-rays, radioactive shoes, gloves, tools, utensils, contaminated furniture and clothing. (Most medical waste ceases to be hazardous in less than a year.) Yet from 1963-1970 someone in the Atomic Energy Commission and/or NECO began to allow waste containing tritium, plutonium and other transuranic elements--from nuclear power and nuclear weapons production plants-- to be brought to the site. (It was accumulating everywhere because of the arms buildup.) In 1970 the Atomic Energy Commission banned transuranic elements from shallow trench burial at the federal sites, but the practice of burying them in the commercial sites continued until 1979. (12) Maxey Flats took in radioactive (and hazardous chemical) waste from all kinds of facilities throughout the eastern United States. When the small boiling-water reactor in Elk River, Minnesota was shut down in 1968, some of its 86,379 cubic feet of waste was sent to Maxey Flats. When the Enrico Fermi I breeder reactor near Detroit was shut down in 1971--after a dangerous near meltdown, described in John Fuller's book *We Almost Lost Detroit* (13)-- the radioactive chips from the disassembling of the fuel were taken to Maxey Flats, as well as steel pipes and liquified wastes from decontamination operations. (14) According to the *Cincinnati Enquirer,* a 40 foot long contaminated railroad tank car was once buried at Maxey Flats. (15) The exact content of all the waste at Maxey Flats isn't known. A story in the *Cincinnati Enquirer* in 1969 gave the impression that the site was meticulously run. The vice-president of NECO said, "Safety is the prime consideration." He said that all items which entered the site were marked according to their degree of radioactivity, that the 17 employees all wore dosimeters, and that the AEC and Kentucky Department of Health made regular monthly visits. (16) This view that Maxey Flats was well-managed, however, does not seem to have been the case. According to a Kentucky state senator investigating the site many years later when the contamination had become a national scandal, "Records from the site are so poor that it would be almost impossible to dig up all the radioactive material because no one is sure where it is located." (17) By the time Maxey Flats closed, there were about 500 pounds of source material (uranium, thorium, or ores containing them) and about 950 pounds of special nuclear material (plutonium, transuranics and enriched uranium). (18) The most dangerous material was put in a 40 acre location at the top of the ridge, known as the Restricted Area.

According to Nancy Powell, a grandmother and later a community activist in Flemingsburg, as early as 1972 people in the community were hearing "shocking stories" about improper operational procedures, accidents and serious safety violations. "Hot" liquid material was sometimes simply dumped over the hillside and into the creek below. On one occasion a liquid waste containing Plutonium-239 was accidentally spilled and eventually drained out of the Restricted Area. There were also rumors of employees salvaging contaminated tools, watches and other items, sometimes for keepsakes, sometimes to sell. (19)

The third major cause of the problems at Maxey Flats was the rainfall. The area is fairly humid; rainfall averages about 46 inches a year. According to Dr. Marvin Resnikoff, who later investigated the contamination for the local citizens' group, the hardness of the surrounding earth caused water to enter the trenches and accumulate. As the rainwater filled the trenches, it mixed with the burial materials and then itself became contaminated. By 1972 it was estimated there were a million gallons of radioactive water at Maxey Flats. (20) (The sites at West Valley and Sheffield had similar problems with contaminated water and also eventually had to be closed.) Said geologist K.S. Shrader-Frechette in her book *Burying Uncertainty: The Case Against the Geological Disposal of Nuclear Waste*,

> For government administrators even to allow Maxey Flats to dump 950 pounds of special nuclear materials (plutonium, Uranium-233, and enriched Uranium-235) in an area with average annual rainfall of 48 inches, in shallow soil trenches 25 feet deep, suggests human error, ignorance, mismanagement or corruption. (21)

iii

In the late 1960s a local farmer named John P. Hayes started one of the first citizen protests against Maxey Flats. According to resident Herbert Jolly, "John P. came into the store in Hillsboro one day and said, 'They're burying stuff up at Maxey Flats that's going to kill all of us.'...Everybody laughed at him, but he kept on until he closed it." (22) Hayes sent water samples to a lab in Minnesota; the readings were so high the lab asked where in the world he had got the water. Jolly remembered the day they went to see Governor Julian Carroll in Frankfort and put a jug of water from Maxey Flats on his desk. Jolly said, "This is what people are drinking down there." (23)

In 1971 citizens of Maxey Flats and Flemingsburg petitioned state health officials to investigate the water which was leaking offsite. Preliminary surveys by the state confirmed the contamination. In 1974 the Atomic Energy Commission stonewalled and said the state was wrong; all was well. It claimed that the plutonium deposited there remained securely in place and guaranteed that it would move no more than *half an inch* over the next 24,000 years. "Deep well water samples," said the report, "at the perimeter of existing licensing burial sites have not shown any detectable plutonium, indicating that the plutonium already buried has remained immobile and therefore constitutes no potential hazard." (24)

A study the same year, however, by the Kentucky Department of Human Resources found that plutonium--far from being "immobile"--had already seeped *off* the burial ground. Rather than moving half an inch in 24,000 years, it had, in less than 10 years, already moved *thousands of feet*, contaminating neighboring properties and stream beds. Later EPA studies confirmed the state's findings. NECO (now called, inexplicably, U. S. Ecology) also claimed that the migration of plutonium was impossible, but the EPA found plutonium approximately three feet deep in core drilling samples. Plutonium was also found in surface soil, in the water of monitoring wells and in drainage streams. (25)

In 1974 citizens formed the Maxey Flats Radiation Protection Association to try to persuade the state to close the site. (One of the activists was Mrs. Regina Carswell.) The group went to the national media to call attention to the contamination. A documentary film was made. The *Washington Star* ran a story January 18, 1976 with the title, "Nuclear Waste Won't Stay Buried." For a time everyone in Washington was talking about Maxey Flats. In the fall of 1977 Tom Wicker wrote about Maxey Flats in the *New York Times*: "In its three decades of existence, the American nuclear power program--pushed with too much zeal and too little concern for the consequences--may have created a Frankenstein's monster that threatens to step out of control." (26)

The governor of Kentucky promised he would close Maxey Flats when there was scientific proof of leakage offsite. In August, 1977 the proof came when state monitoring investigations confirmed that radioactive leachate was seeping from a newly opened trench in the Restricted Area. (27) The Kentucky legislature, still not comprehending the vastness of the problem, did not want to give up the site. They decided to impose a ten-cent per pound surcharge on the waste to discourage any more from coming in. Soon it was clear to everyone, however, that the site as a commercial enterprise was finished. (28)

iv

In December, 1977 the state of Kentucky formally closed Maxey Flats. The state paid NECO/ US Ecology $1.27 million for the closing, with the stipulation that NECO would continue to monitor the site for the next 13 months. Unfortunately the state had been given bad advice about its original contract with NECO, for the contract absolved the company of any liability in respect to the contamination. (The state of Illinois, which had also had a deal with NECO for the Sheffield site, did not have such an indemnity clause.) (29)   A few years later NECO billed the state for *another* million dollars for cleanup activities during this 13 month oversight period (and the courts said the state had to pay). (30)

From 1977 to 1988 the state of Kentucky spent over $1 million a year trying to deal with the water in the trenches and the contaminated water which was leaking offsite. In the early 1970s it had tried an evaporation system to get rid of the trench water, but the system had only been able to remove about half of it. Furthermore, the evaporation spread steam contaminated with tritium throughout the countryside. Westinghouse, which had assumed management of the site after NECO left, pumped out millions of gallons of radioactive water and stored the leftover sludge above ground. (31)   In 1980, as a temporary remedial measure, 85% of the trenches were covered with huge sheets of plastic to reduce the amount of water coming in. The plastic was fragile, however; winds tore it, birds and animals pecked holes in it; workers had to spend a great deal of time looking for the holes. (32)

In 1983 surveys of the site showed new problems. Analyses of water in the trenches showed tritium, as well as dissolved Cobalt-60, Cesium-137, Strontium-90 and plutonium, though only tritium and plutonium had migrated underground appreciably. According to Dr. Resnikoff, the chemical EDTA had interacted with the radionuclides and perhaps was what had caused them to migrate. Tritium levels offsite were up to 1,830 times what was permissible; Strontium-90 levels, 1,000 times. In March, 1983 tritium was detected in the sap of nearby maple trees--perhaps due to the spread of particles from the evaporation process, perhaps from absorption from the soil. The highest concentration of tritium in tree sap came from trees closest to a trench which contained a DOE nuclear warhead refurbishing operation from Mound. Tritium was also discovered in domestic well waters and the milk samples of nearby cows. (33)

Meanwhile state legislators argued about various decommissioning plans and plans for the long-term cleanup. The federal Low-Level Radioactive Waste Policy Act of 1980 had mandated that states set up regional compacts to store their low-level wastes in one regional center (a system which did not work and still is not working, because no state has wanted to assume the radioactive waste for a whole region). Kentucky made a tentative agreement to form a compact with the state of Illinois, but only for the radwaste from its two medical colleges: Illinois didn't want anything to do with the waste from Maxey Flats. Nor did anyone else. It was finally clear to everyone that the waste at Maxey Flats was going to have to stay where it was. (34)

In 1990, 13 years after the closing of the site, Governor Wallace Wilkinson finally approved a 100-year plan for "containing and strict monitoring" of the 475 million cubic feet of radioactive waste at Maxey Flats. Everyone understood that the site could never be "cleaned up;" it would always be radioactive. Nor could the contaminated soil be dug up and transferred elsewhere, as had been done at Mound, Paducah, Piketon, Fernald and other places; the contamination was too deep. All the state could do was try to contain the waste as best it could so the radioactive elements didn't migrate. (35) At the request of the Citizens Advisory Board, the state acquired a 300 acre buffer zone around the site property. (36) The immediate remediation was to be supervised by the EPA, but the long-term care of the site will finally be the responsibility of the state of Kentucky.

In the late 1980s Kentucky had approached the EPA with the idea of having Maxey Flats put on the National Priorities List and designated a Superfund site, so that it could get federal assistance with the enormous costs of the remediation. Initially the EPA refused; up till then all the Superfunds had gone to chemically-polluted locations including a notorious illegal hazardous waste dump, the "Valley of the Drums," on the Smith Farm in Bullitt County, Kentucky. (37) Maxey Flats became the first nuclear waste site granted Superfund status. The Superfund was basically a trust fund set up through a corporate tax on industries. (The tax expired in 1995, was not renewed by Congress, and the fund today is empty; cleanups from now on will be paid for by taxpayers, not corporations.) But in the late 1980s a remediation plan was worked out collaboratively between the EPA, state officials, industries and the Citizens Advisory Board of Flemingsburg to pay for the first stage of the Maxey Flats cleanup.

More than 400 companies, universities, and hospitals, including Ohio State, P&G and the University of Cincinnati--which had all sent materials to Maxey Flats--were taxed to help pay for the remediation; money came as well from the Army, Air Force, DOE and NASA. In 1995 when the EPA settlement was finally reached, the state of Kentucky was enormously relieved. Said former state senator Ed Ford of Cynthiana, who had worked for years on the settlement: "I can attribute several of these multiple gray hairs to Maxey Flats."(38)

v

There had been disagreement, however, even among the scientists, about what remediation methods to use. The EPA had wanted to experiment with a "compaction" method, where barrels of waste would be crushed to extract water, which would then be solidified in concrete. Other scientists, though, thought this method unproven and potentially dangerous, so the state rejected it. (39) In June, 1995 two Consent Decrees ("one for the 50 *de maximis* parties and one for the 306 *de minimis* parties") arranged for cost allocation and for the performance of the Remedial Design and Remedial Action. (40) International Technology Corporation, based in Torrance, California, was awarded a multi-million contract to design remedial methods: groundwater modeling, extracting leachate from the trenches and solidifying it, decontaminating the buildings, installing erosion control structures. (41) (IT also worked on the cleanup at Fernald.) The remediating firms pumped nearly a million gallons of contaminated water from the old trenches, then mixed it with cement and additives. This mixture was then poured into new, specially constructed, earth-mounded concrete bunkers to solidify. Surface drainage water controls and erosion controls were also established, to minimize further water accumulation. Eventually the whole area was covered with an "Interim Cap," a heavy vinyl sheet, under which the waste will be allowed to subside or settle. (42) Intensive monitoring of the area will have to go on for at least a hundred years. In 1995 *Kentucky Post* reporter Peggy Kreimer, visiting the vast empty space of Maxey Flats, now covered with black plastic, found an eerie mingling of Kentucky's rural past and nuclear present: "Attached to the rusting and sometimes weather-bent fence posts were wooden boxes that hold burbling beakers and electric monitoring equipment which continually tests the air." (43)

The remediation was not without incident. In 1989 two accidents caused the work to shut down. In one case a hose squirted out water contaminated by tritium during a pressure test, splattering all over one worker; two days later a worker punctured a plastic liner and six gallons of hazardous waste mixed with concrete leaked out. (44) In 1990 two scientists, John Volpe and Paul Kerlisz, who had been setting up a system to monitor the movement of tritium off site, discovered ground water with radiation up to five times the legal limit seeping from a new spring on the east hillside below Maxey Flats. Volpe said it was not an imminent threat to residents, "unless you drink it." (45) In 1999 an accident occurred when a valve was removed from a hose which was releasing tritium-laced water from a trench into a bunker. The water backed up into the trench and overflowed, causing about 8,700 gallons of contaminated water to escape. Though the EPA said it was not dangerous, some Kentucky officials were worried, and Nancy Powell said, "My group and I are concerned that these bunkers are not what they're cracked up to be, and they're not going to hold up." (46)

In 2003, however, a Certificate of Completion was issued by the federal EPA. The Interim Cap over the new trench bunkers was in place. A six foot barbed wire fence was put up to keep out people and animals. The cost of the immediate remediation was over $100 million dollars. (47) In 2003 the Kentucky Division of Waste Management assumed responsibility for the future monitoring and maintenance of the site: fence repair, drainage channel maintenance, subsidence monitoring, monitoring of surface and groundwater, interim cap repair (and replacement --at least every twenty years, more often if necessary). (48) According to a September, 2005 report of the Kentucky Interagency Groundwater Monitoring Network, the U.S. Geological Survey is providing technical assistance to the Division of Waste Management in monitoring the water. The USGS maintains *continuous* water level data recorders in 15 monitoring wells at the site. Five of these monitoring wells are also sampled semi-annually for tritium concentrations. Water levels are periodically measured at 14 other monitoring wells; of these, two are sampled quarterly for tritium and the other 12 sampled annually. (49) After 100 years, if no major leaks or problems have occurred, and EPA studies indicate that the materials have subsided to sufficient radioactive levels, the plan is to have the whole site covered with a final multi-layered engineered cap and then covered with earth, similar to plans for the hill at Fernald. For thousands of years thereafter it will be the responsibility of the state of Kentucky--or someone--to continue monitoring the radiation levels.

vi

With the immediate remediation coming to an end, Nancy Powell, speaking for the Maxey Flats Concerned Citizens, said:

> It's all worked out as well as could be expected....It will never be perfect, but it's sure a lot better than it was. We're all tired. It's been long, long years. I don't think we'll ever feel perfectly good about the dump. We'll always worry about it. But is not something we dwell on. We've done everything we can do.(50)

About 300 residents still live within five miles of the Restricted Area. (51)

An EPA report on Maxey Flats will be issued every five years. The first report in 2002 indicated "no unacceptable exposure potential under current conditions," though what is meant by "unacceptable" is not explained. (52) In the summer of 2002 public hearings were held by the state Environmental Quality Commission in Morehead, Kentucky to give residents a chance to ask questions of state officials. The summary of one of these hearings reveals the residents were still concerned about the tritium levels in the drinking water, though they were told the water was safe. They asked if tests had been done on fish or wildlife, but were told data indicated there was no need for them (and the tests were expensive). Several asked questions about the expense of the monitoring, fearful that at some point the state might simply stop paying for the oversight. One official said one way for the state to save money would be to stop printing and mailing out the annual reports, a remark with uncomfortable overtones. All of the responses to the residents' questions (as presented in the report) were short and abrupt; nothing about the data was explained in detail. (53) According to an Earth Day article about an open house at Maxey Flats in April, 2006, there is no contaminated water outside Maxey Flat's restricted area today, "except for two springs in the buffer zone where low levels have been detected," something which is not completely reassuring. (54) In the spring of 2006 a local columnist expressed what is evidently an ongoing community worry, that "nobody knows how much plutonium is leaking out of Maxey Flats." (55)

The second Five-Year Review of Maxey Flats was released in September 2007, which concluded that the monitoring program was working. ("No deficiencies that affect the protectiveness of the remedy were noted.") The state of

Kentucky seemed to be pressing for an earlier final closing of the site, in part because "subsistance in the trenches has been significantly lower than antici- pated" (and also the monitoring of the Interim Cap is very expensive.) (56)

Today only three licensed low-level radioactive waste disposal sites pres- ently exist. The two in Richland, Washington and Barnwell, South Carolina are still operating. Both will soon only be taking in waste from agreed-upon states within their region. The third site is the private facility Envirocare (Energy So- lutions) in Utah, which, as said before, is now taking in B and C level waste from all over the country, as well as A level. Utah environmentalists are watch- ing Envirocare carefully and regularly report on its safety violations. (57)

In 1994 U.S. Ecology (formerly NECO) applied to operate a new low-level radioactive waste site in Ward Valley in the Mojave Desert of California. A U.S. Geological Survey said that, even though the area was dry, there was not enough evidence that the soil was impermeable, and there were fears that aqui- fer contamination deep beneath the site might contaminate the Colorado River, a major drinking water source for southern California. One of the reasons local activists opposed the site was US Ecology's notorious management history at Beatty, Sheffield, and Maxey Flats. Said Senator Barbara Boxer, "Every site that they've run has leaked. They've left a mess wherever they've gone. Their record I think would give anyone pause." (58) In 1998 Ward Valley was re- fused a license, and though U.S. Ecology continued with court fights, it seemed in 2002 to have given up. (59)

In the early 1990s the Department of Energy tried to locate an "interim" high level nuclear waste site in Kentucky, this time, a storage facility for the spent fuel rods from nuclear reactors, which they said would only be located in the state temporarily until the permanent site--presumably Yucca Mountain-- opened. The DOE offered improved highways, money for public schools, health care and recreation programs, tax subsidies and direct cash payments. They even offered $200,000 to any community which would allow them to do a feasibility study. Union County, Kentucky turned them down, but some offi- cials in Crittenden County in western Kentucky expressed interest in the $200,000. The study could not take place, however, without the governor's ap- proval, and Democratic Governor Brereton Jones said no. There were fears the "temporary" location might become permanent. Phillip Shepherd, then the Sec- retary of Natural Resources, said, "I think it is cynical of the federal government to try to solve this [waste] problem by playing on the needs of rural communities and poverty-stricken areas." (60)

Such an attitude is far different from that of the Kentucky politicians today who have fought to *get* funds for feasibility studies for storing and perhaps reprocessing high-level radioactive waste. The Energy and Water Appropriations Bill for 2007 even stipulates that when a site for the reprocessing/storage of waste is chosen, governors, states, or local citizens may have little right to oppose it, as Kentucky, for instance, did in the past. The federal government would invoke "eminent domain" to put the waste where it wanted. Bobbie Ann Mason has recently mourned the turning of the rural farmlands of Kentucky into repositories for the "world's poisons"--the sludge from the Martin County coal accident in 2000, the chemical weapons stockpile at the Bluegrass Army Depot at Richmond, and now the possibility of high-level waste in Paducah. (61) How the state responds to these latest nuclear plans may be one of the major Kentucky stories of the next decade. As if what happened at Maxey Flats weren't warning enough.

Notes: Maxey Flats

1. McCutcheon, Chuck, *Nuclear Reactions: The Politics of Opening a Radioactive Waste Disposal Site* (Albuquerque: University of New Mexico Press, 2002), 7.

2. "Atom Power Curb Seen," *New York Times* April 6, 1955, 25.

3. "Radioactive Waste." *Backgrounder: U.S. Nuclear Regulatory Commission*, March 2005. (www.nrc.gov/reading-rm/doc-collections/fact-sheets/radwaste.html)

4. Shapiro, Fred C., *Radwaste: A Reporter's Investigation of a Growing Nuclear Menace* (New York: Random House, 1981), 123-127.

5. "States Oppose Plan for Atomic Waste," *New York Times,* December 28, 1961, 11.

6. Shrader-Frechette, K. S. *Burying Uncertainty: Risk and the Case Against Geological Disposal of Nuclear Waste* (Berkeley: University of California Press, 1993), 59, 64-65.

7. "Kentucky NPL/NPL Caliber Cleanup Site Summaries." U.S. Environmental Protection Agency (www.epa.gov/cgi-bin/eraprintonly.cgi).

8. Powell, Nancy, "A Concerned Community," *EPA Journal,* 17 (July/August, 1991), 31.

9. Powell 31.

10. Kreimer, Peggy, "Maxey Flats--The Nuclear Legacy," *Kentucky Post,* July 8, 1995, 1K.

11. Bartlett, Donald and James B. Steele, *Forevermore: Nuclear Waste in America* (New York: W. W. Norton, 1985), 198-199.

12. Bartlett and Steele 50.

13. Fuller, John G. *We Almost Lost Detroit.* New York: Reader's Digest Press, 1975.

14. Shapiro 177, 172.

15. "Land Above Serene, but Fleming 'Graveyard' Broils," *Cincinnati Enquirer,* January 3, 1969, 14.

16. "Land Above" 14.

17. Chellgren, Mark R., "State May Get Superfund Aid to Help Clean Up Maxey Flats," *Lexington Herald-Leader,* March 7, 1985, B2.

18. "Kentucky NPL."

19. Powell 31.

20. Resnikoff, Marvin, *Living without Landfills: Confronting the 'Low-Level' Radiation Crisis* (New York: Radioactive Waste Campaign, 1987), 35.

21. Shrader-Frechette 71.

22. Warren, Jim, "For Earth Day, An Open House at Nuclear Dump," *Lexington Herald-Leader,* April 23, 2006, B1.

23. Warren, "For Earth Day" B1.

24. Quoted in Bartlett and Steele 46.

25. Resnikoff 35.

26. Wicker, Tom, "Paying the Nuclear Piper," *New York Times,* September 27, 1977, 39.

27. Resnikoff 35.

28. Shapiro 148.

29. Warren, Jim, "Maxey Flats Still in a Holding Pattern," *Lexington Herald-Leader,* July 5, 1983, A1.

30. "Judge: State Owes Maxey Flats Contractor $1 Million," *Lexington Herald-Leader,* July 21, 1993, B4.

31. Resnikoff 36.

32. Warren, "Maxey Flats Still" A1.

33. Resnikoff 36.

34. Brammer, Jack, "Bill Would Send Kentucky Radioactive Waste to Illinois," *Lexington Herald-Leader,* January 9, 1986, B3.

35. "Maxey Flats Cleanup Plan Garners Favorable Reactions from All Sides," *Lexington Herald-Leader,* February 11, 1990, B1.

36. Powell 31.

37. "Maxey Flats, Bullitt Waste Site on List for Federal Cleanup," *Lexington Herald-Leader,* September 22, 1984, B1.

38. Main, Frank and Dan Hassert, "Maxey Flats: The End," *Kentucky Post,* July 6, 1995, 1K

39. "State Rejects Cleanup Proposals for Maxey Flats," *Lexington Herald-Leader,* October 12, 1989, B3.

40. "Kentucky NPL/NPL Caliber Cleanup Site Summaries," United States Environmental Protection Agency (www.epa.gov/region4waste/npl/nplky/maxfltky.htm).

41. "International Technology Corporation Awarded Multi-Million Dollar Contract at Maxey Flats Disposal Site," *PR Newswire,* July 25, 1995, 725.

42. "Maxey Flats Disposal Site, Fleming County Kentucky" Fact Sheet Update. U.S. Environmental Protection Agency, Region IV, Atlanta, Georgia. October 2001. (www.epa.gov/region04/waste/npl/nplky/maxfltky.htm).

43. Kreimer 1K.

44. "Maxey Flats Nuclear Waste Cleanup Resumes This Week," *Lexington Herald-Leader,* July 23, 1989.

45. Wagar, Kit, "Radiation Found in Water at Dump," *Lexington Herald-Leader,* September 21, 1990, A1.

46. "Radioactive Waste Dump Spill Frightens Residents," *Kentucky Post,* May 12, 1999, 1K.

47. "Cleanup of Nuclear Dump Nearly Finished," *Louisville Courier-Journal,* November 8, 2002.

48. Minutes of Public Meeting of the Environmental Quality Commission, Morehead State University, Morehead, Kentucky, May 31, 2002. (http://e-archives.ky.gov/minutes/eqc/meeting02/53102minutes.PDF)

49. Fisher, Stephen R. "Environmental Report 2004-2005: Kentucky Inter-agency Groundwater Management Network." September, 2005. (www.uky.edu/kegs/water/gnet/04-05gnet.pdf)

50. Alford, Roger, "Nuclear Dump Site Cleanup Nears End," *Lexington Herald-Leader,* December 22, 2001, C1.

51. "Kentucky NPL."

52. "First Five Year Review Report for Maxey Flats Disposal Site, Fleming County, Kentucky." September 2002. (http://www.epa.gov/region4/waste/sf/fiveyear.htm)

53. "Minutes of Public Meeting."

54. Warren, Jim, "For Earth Day" B1.

55. Sloan, Bob, "Elected Officials Ignore Real Problems," *Lexington Herald-Leader,* July 4, 2006, A9.

56. "Second 5-Year EPA Review of Maxey Flats," September, 2007. (OASpub.epa.gov/enviro/cerclis_web.report?PGN_SYS_ID=KYD980729107.)

57. See the website of the Healthy Environment Alliance of Utah (www.healutah.org/what/envirocare/factsheet.html) and the website of the Utah Downwinders (www.downwinders.org).

58. Hastings, Deborah, "Not in Our Back Yard: Nuclear-Materials Mishandler's Efforts to Build California Waste Dump Opposed," *Cleveland Plain Dealer,* May 20, 1996, 7D.

59. Harrison, Tom, "American Ecology Posts 2003 Loss due to Ward Valley Write-Off," *Nucleonics Week* 45 (February 19, 2004), 5.

60. Mead, Andy, "Jones: No More Nuclear Waste," *Lexington Herald-Leader,* September 19, 1992, A1.

61. Mason, Bobbie Ann, "Pick Your Poison," *New York Times,* October 29, 2006.

The Littered Battleground:
Jefferson Proving Ground,
Southeastern Indiana

Jefferson Proving Ground in southern Indiana was not part of the DOE nuclear weapons production cycle, as most of the other sites discussed here were, yet fifty years of military bombardment of the land created extensive environmental damage. And from 1984-1995 Jefferson *did* test weapons with depleted uranium, so it is now also part of the nuclear history of the region. According to Dr. Doug Rokke, Jefferson Proving Ground may be one of the most contaminated depleted uranium sites in the world. (1) The full significance of this legacy is still not yet understood. Depleted uranium has a half-life of 4.5 billion years.

In the early 1800s Southern Indiana was first settled by European immigrants who established large farms and planted orchards. Rural towns were small--even into the 20th century--sometimes consisting only of a general store, church, and one-room school house. The residents were known to be proud, hard-working, and religious. In the 1930s the war department sent surveyors into the area to look for a site to test munitions. The army location in Aberdeen, Maryland was beginning to be seen as too small and too near urban populations. After surveying several locations the army finally selected a wedge-shaped area of land--90 square miles--which cut through Jefferson, Ripley and Jennings counties in southern Indiana. The site was seven miles north of the Ohio River. On Friday December 6, 1940--a year before Pearl Harbor--federal, state and local officials gathered at the Jefferson County court house and announced that the army was going to take over the land. More than six hundred residents had a month's time to sell their farms and leave. (2)

As at Fernald, the initial reaction of the farmers was one of confusion, resentment and shock. Churches were filled to capacity. One woman said of her father, "He was devastated by the news, especially the deadline which proved unrealistic and had to be extended. I think it contributed to his death, which was less than a year later." (3) The daughter of another resident said of her father that the experience had been "heart-breaking." "[He] was an old German and they practically had to carry him out of the house." (4) Every day people gathered in the streets and talked about what was happening. Rev. Dahlgren Casey of the Marble Corner Methodist Church, who had often read Mrs. Roosevelt's "My Day" column, wrote her asking for help -- thinking her perhaps more approachable than her husband--but she cabled back she could do nothing.

> I realize what a sacrifice it is to give up your church and how difficult it is to wrench oneself away from families and beloved surroundings. I send my best wishes for happiness in the future.(5)

Rev. Casey read the cable to his congregation the next Sunday. Although six area residents refused to comply with the army orders, everyone else did. On February 16, 1941 nearly 1,200 people gathered for the final service at St. Magdalena Church, a large beautiful limestone structure, which would be destroyed a few years later during a practice bombing raid.

Few of the residents were fairly compensated for their land. The real estate and title companies in Indianapolis which the army had contacted to oversee the land sales often charged exorbitant commission fees. (6) One man received only $7,500 dollars for 200 acres of farmland. (7) The religious also worried about what would happen to their cemeteries: it was as difficult to find new homes for the dead as the living. Phyllis May, whose parents had lost their farm, remembered many years later: "Most of the people that came out of there had bad feelings about it. They weren't given an equal chance to defend themselves. They had no say in it whatsoever. It was just something they were ordered to do." (8) The most luxurious homes in the area were kept as buildings to be used by the army staff, including "Old Timbers," the summer retreat lodge of a wealthy Cincinnati businessman named Alexander Thomson. (9) Some area residents later did find civilian jobs when the Proving Ground opened. Some also went to work during the war at the DuPont Smokeless Powder Plant (a gunpowder factory) in Charlestown, Indiana, about 30 miles south on the river. Rural community life, however, had been destroyed.

ii

The Proving Ground consisted of 55,265 acres. In late January, 1941 the Army began constructing 120 buildings ("typical factory structures") using bricks and timber from the land. Nineteen recovery and observation fields--3,000 to 16,000 yards from the firing point--were laid out, and concrete observation shelters built and covered with rocks and earth so that they resembled small hills. (10) There were sixty-four miles of railroad track and a small airport; the whole site was surrounded by a 50-mile chain-link fence. The estimated cost of the installation was $12 million dollars. (11)

The first munitions were test-fired in May, 1941. From 1941-1945 the base tested all kinds of weapons, 24 hours a day, 7 days a week. All of the structures from the old communities were decimated. "'Churches or whatever, we torched it, bulldozed it and bombed it,' said Randall Rogers, who had been a munitions tester in 1942. 'We saw horror stories that the people who left never knew.'" (12) Bags of gunpowder were brought in from Charlestown for testing. A worker named Leroy Harsin remembered many years later that he had once been the director for tests of a navy torpedo. His crew had constructed a 40-foot wooden tower, from which the torpedo had been dropped. It blew up all the structures, he said, and didn't have to be tested again. (13) By 1944, the 100,000th round of ammunition had been fired. Residents in nearby Madison had by then become accustomed to the booms. At peak times people said the windows in Madison would rattle and dishes would shake. If some thought at the start that the Proving Ground would simply be a place where guns were tested, they soon learned otherwise. The technology of modern warfare had become extremely sophisticated. According to a report issued years later by the Indiana Department of Environmental Management, a wide range of munitions and ordnance were tested there: propellants, mines, ammunition, cartridge cases, artillery projectiles, mortar rounds, grenades, tank ammunition, bombs, boosters and rockets. (14) Not only ground weapons but also air weapons were tested. Fire bombs used to destroy the old Bethel Church and St. Magdalena were of the kind later used to destroy Tokyo, Osaka and other cities in Japan. Major General Charles Sweeney, a test pilot at Jefferson in the early years of the war, later flew the B-29 which dropped the bomb on Nagasaki. (15)

At the end of the war Kenneth R. Merchant of Madison was hired to do the first "cleanup" of the grounds. His crew went through the grounds looking for

UXO (unexploded ordnance) and managed to detect and destroy thousands of them. (16) The Proving Ground didn't close, but was put on "caretaker" status; in between World War II and Korea some of the buildings were leased to factories. In 1951, however, when the Korean War began, the tests resumed, and once again residents heard the booming, window-shattering sounds. Employment peaked in 1953 when there were 1,774 workers; testing went on 24 hours a day. (17) (*The New York Times* reported that in 1955 a 30 year old man from Cincinnati once climbed over the fence and lived inside the firing range for three weeks, "making a religious retreat," he said, living on pears and apples. None of the shells touched him.) (18)

Much of the ordnance tested at the site in the early years was made in Cincinnati. According to the *Cincinnati Times-Star*, $70,000,000 of the billion-dollar munitions business came from 16 firms in the Cincinnati Ordnance District. This story, like others of the time, emphasized the benefits of the military to the Cincinnati economy. (19) The Proving Ground stayed open until 1958, then went to "caretaker" status again, opening in the 1960s during the Vietnam War.

iii

When the war ended some thought the Testing Ground might close, but it didn't. It wasn't until 1984, however, that the Nuclear Regulatory Commission licensed the Army to begin testing ammunition made from depleted uranium. As said earlier, Fernald had first worked on the development of DU ammunition in the 1970s, using some of the great quantities of uranium hexafluoride which was sitting in barrels in Paducah and Piketon, the refuse from the enrichment operation. Though U-238 is called depleted because it is not fissionable, it is still 60% as radioactive as natural uranium. Converting the depleted uranium into weapons was cheap (because so much was available) and also convenient, helping the DOE deal with the dangerous Paducah/Piketon waste problem (though as said before, radioactive dangers do not disappear but simply take on different forms). Solidified, depleted uranium is very, very hard, 65% more dense than lead, with the capacity to cut easily through other metals--"like a knife through butter," the army said. The most common DU weapons in the US arsenal were the 120 mm shells fired by M-1 tanks, and the 30 mm shells fired by A-10 aircraft. (20) Weapons using depleted uranium were first used heavily in the Gulf War--almost 320 tons of depleted uranium were left in Iraq--(21) and later in Kosovo, Afghanistan and the current Iraq War, usage of which has created a controversy worldwide.

From 1984-1994 the army at the Proving Ground fired more than 77 tons of depleted uranium projectiles into a 2,000-acre area known as the Delta Impact Area, or later the Depleted Uranium Impact Area. According to the Jefferson Proving Ground website, DU penetrators were tested to track firing, flight trajectory and accuracy of the anti-tank weapons. The DU Impact Area is where the DU penetrators, or their fragments, eventually stopped, after having been fired from one of the three positions several miles down range. (22) The Army has said that DU rounds being tested for trajectory were fired into canvas targets stretched across telephone poles on the southern edge of the Delta Impact area, and that they were not tested against metal, (though that is how the ammunition was used in anti-tank weapons in Iraq). (23) An article in the *Cincinnati Enquirer* in 1985, however, suggests that some testing against metal did take place. A Proving Ground commander said in an interview that some ammunition was being tested against "6-inch thick steel targets," simulating "the thickness of Russian tanks." The reporter noticed that "the steel could have been ¼ inch drywall the way the shells ripped through them." Though the article doesn't say they were DU shells, this description certainly sounds like the cut-through-butter effect of depleted uranium anti-tank ammunition (and the date is right). (24)

Why the testing against metal is so significant is that when a shell made out of DU hits a hard target, it ignites with tremendous heat and produces a tiny ceramic radioactive dust of uranium oxide particles, which can travel in the air and be dangerous if inhaled by people nearby. The particles ultimately settle on the land or in the water of the area. (25) If DU *was* tested against metal at Jefferson, uranium oxide particles may have fallen on the ground and may have become part of the ecosystem. (The article about the metal-testing at Jefferson is not listed in the *Enquirer* Index; I found it when looking through microfilm for articles on Fernald.)

There is also the "Paducah" factor, that is, some of the ammunition tested may have been made from depleted uranium from Paducah which was contaminated with plutonium and other transuranic elements. Recently the government has admitted that some of the DU weapons which went to Iraq did have traces of plutonium, though it claims not enough to be dangerous. (26) There is no way to know how many of the projectiles tested at Jefferson may have contained transuranic contamination, but given the volume of the testing (77 tons), it is likely some were; that is, there may be traces of plutonium in the soil as well as uranium.

Officially the Army has always maintained that there is no radiological hazard from the depleted uranium at the Proving Ground. According to the JPG website, "The major health concerns about DU relate to its chemical properties as a heavy metal, rather than to its radioactivity, which is low." It's true that DU is chemically toxic, and drinking water contaminated with DU may cause kidney damage, but a 2002 Royal Society study in England showed that a number of soldiers in Iraq who worked near or on tanks using DU ammunition may have died of lung cancer after having inhaled the DU dust. (27) Dr. Rosalie Bertell believes that the Gulf War Syndrome in American soldiers--sometimes attributed to exposure to depleted uranium-- may have come about because of the synergistic effects of the DU with other substances: vaccines, pesticides, parasites, toxic smoke inhalation, the destruction of the Iraqi chemical factories, and EMF on the battlefield. She believes that long term low-level exposure to DU may have more serious genetic consequences than immediate high levels of exposure. (28) Dr. Alexandra Miller of the Armed Forces Radiobiology Institute is also studying the possible synergistic effects of DU's toxic and radiological qualities. Some of her early work showed that DU damaged chromosomes within cultured cells, which may have implications for further cancer and genetic studies. (29) Cancer and birth defects in southern Iraq near Basra, where bombing in the first Gulf War was heaviest, have increased 300% since 1991. Childhood leukemia has skyrocketed. Iraqi physicians believe these illnesses and deaths have all the indications of having been radiologically-induced. (30) Leonard Dietz, a physicist for Knolls Atomic Power Laboratory, has noted that when DU ten times the permissible level was discovered in the area of the National Lead plant at Colonie, New York (the plant discussed in the Fernald chapter), the government closed down the factory. Dietz said, "To protect the health of Americans we shut down a factory discharging the equivalent of about two 30 mm shells into the atmosphere. How can we justify using a million shells in Iraq and Kuwait, most of it only in four days of war?" (31)

Much of the research about the health effects of DU is still in the early stages. It is made more difficult by the fact that the Pentagon refuses to test all soldiers who were in Iraq for uranium; by the fact that some of the health centers in Iraq where records were kept have been bombed; and by the fact that the Iraqi landscape is still contaminated by chemicals and other residues of war. Enough information exists, however, to raise questions about the army's claim that the DU exploded at the Proving Ground was not radiologically dangerous, particularly given the amount of depleted uranium--in fragments, perhaps in particles-- now in the ground and potentially affecting the water and ecosystem. As one southern Indiana resident said recently, "They just don't know." (32)

iv

The Proving Ground was officially closed in 1989, as part of the Base Re-alignment and Closure Act (BRAC) which was passed by both houses of Congress with little debate. The closing of 145 bases was presented as an action which would save the federal government money and streamline military efficiency. Munitions testing was to be moved from Jefferson to Yuma, Arizona. According to the BRAC study, the cost of closure and relocation would be recovered in six years; the land at Jefferson could be cleaned up and sold for a profit. The report noted that there might be some environmental problems, but "this review was not intended to be a substitute for the environmental analysis." (33) No substitute indeed. When the Indiana Department of Environmental Management did an analysis the next year of how much it would cost to clean up the Proving Ground (to the point where it could be used again), they discovered the environmental contamination was so extensive a complete cleanup was economically impossible. It's hard to believe that the army didn't know this at the time of BRAC. In addition to the 77 tons of DU and the 1.5 million rounds of UXO in the soil, there were other environmental problems: lost munitions possibly buried or dumped in nearby wells; seven landfills, two of which contained solvents; five surface impoundments; 14 chemical disposal sites; 15 storage and 40 herbicide application areas; and 54 underground storage tanks, some of which were leaking. A Battelle Memorial Institute report said initially that a total cleanup of Jefferson would cost $8.4 billion and "$15.9 billion if all the breaks went the wrong way." (34)

Other military bases being closed throughout the country faced similar massive problems with environmental contamination. It was becoming clear, in fact, as one reporter said, that the Department of Defense had in fact become, perhaps had always been, "America's most pervasive and protected polluter." (35) It was estimated in 1991 that the cleanup of all the BRAC bases alone--apart from everything else in the military budget--would be close to $400 *billion* dollars. (36) About this time an article appeared in *Newsweek*.

Nowhere is the Pentagon's environmental nightmare more vivid than at the Army's Jefferson Proving Ground in southern Indiana. Since 1941 workers have test-fired 23 million artillery, mortar and tank rounds across 90 square miles of forests and wildflower meadows. An estimated 1.4 million of those test rounds haven't exploded--yet. Shells protrude menacingly from the ground, others have burrowed as far as 24 feet below. There are also armor-piercing rounds made of uranium and munitions containing white phosphorus, which ignites on contact with air. "Poke your nose in the Army's business and you might disappear," says Jane Hance, whose farmhouse windows rattle with the thunder of steady cannonades. "They don't even know what they've got over there." (37)

Initially word of the closing hit area residents hard because over 400 jobs would be lost. Indiana politicians also made token cries of protest. The residents were even more outraged, however, when they learned about the radioactive and toxic contamination and the exorbitant cost of the cleanup. Said Madison Mayor Morris Wooden: "Grade school math tells you that the Army won't want to remove this UXO. But we are determined not to let them walk away from this ground they seized 49 years ago." (38)

Residents began to gather to discuss their options. At one point Mayor Wooden said he thought the base should just remain open. "They're going to go out there to Yuma and do the same damn thing they did to us environmentally." (39) State and local politicians soon realized, however, that the closing was inevitable. In 1992 a Lexington engineering firm Mason & Hanger signed an agreement with the army to begin a cleanup of the Proving Ground. (40) In 1995 the base finally closed, and the Jefferson Proving Ground Redevelopment Board was formed. Residents hoped that part of the land could be cleaned up and salvaged, particularly the 3,000 acres *south* of the firing line--the army headquarters area. In 1996 the NRC announced that an independent radiological study had confirmed that these 3,000 acres were safe and could be released for unrestricted use. Madison submitted a redevelopment plan to the federal government, but it was turned down, after which the army decided simply to auction off the property. A local Madison businessman named Dean Ford, who had grown up on the edges of the Proving Ground, bought the land for $5.1 million. Though some in the area hoped a large employer could be found, Ford immediately began to parcel up the property. Thirty-four acres were sold to the state of Indiana to build a state highway garage. Buildings and farmlands were leased; a few businesses opened, including a restaurant. (41) (Ten years later FEMA bought land from Ford to store mobile homes and trailers used for disasters.) (42)

ν

There was uncertainty, however, about what was going to happen to the rest of the Proving Ground--most of it, in fact. The Army couldn't sell the 51,000 acres above the firing line because of liability issues connected with the UXO. The rounds of unexploded ordnance themselves were dangerous. Col. Dennis O'Brien of the Proving Ground said, "Nobody has a clue how much stuff we have down range....After 50 years of gunplay 1.5 million rounds of UXO lie scattered on the ground or buried up to 30 feet below the surface. The army's white phosphorus shells--which burn white-hot--are certain to ignite if ever exhumed." (43)

Furthermore, the depleted uranium was a huge problem. The Army said it was too dangerous to go in and try to collect any intact DU projectiles because of the UXO. If DU fragments were imbedded in the earth (or if uranium particles *had* settled on the soil), any kind of soil removal would also be too dangerous to do because of the UXO. (44) (When the Nuclear Regulatory Commission had given the Proving Ground its license, Save the Valley, a local environmental group, had asked then if it was a good idea to fire uranium ammunition into live fields, knowing it could not easily be retrieved, but their warning had not been heeded.) (45)

While all these discussions about the future of the grounds were going on, the Indiana Air National Guard continued to use the central part of the Proving Ground for target practice on the weekends. In 1997 the Army signed a three-year Memorandum of Agreement with the U.S. Fish and Wildlife Service to oversee and manage the site. Much of the Proving Ground was regarded by biologists as an "ecological treasure," because it contained hundreds of acres of unbroken forests, lakes, wetlands, caves, rare plants, and different species of fish, reptiles and amphibians. Plans were discussed to turn the Proving Ground into a permanent wildlife reserve (similar to the current plans for Fernald). In the summer of 1999, however, the Air Force proposed that it be allowed to take over most of the site --40,000 acres of it--because it needed a large space to train Air National Guard F-16 fighters in the use of laser-guided "smart-bombs." (46) In the Air Force plan the wildlife refuge would only be a small 10,000 acre region in the northernmost part of the site. Though initially the Army seemed receptive to the Air Force idea, strong opposition to the plan from the Fish and Wildlife Service and from local politicians led them to abandon it.

In the final agreement the Fish and Wildlife Service was given jurisdiction over 40,000 acres of the site (though 30,000 would be totally off-limits). The Indiana Air National Guard would only control two targets on about 1,000 acres near the middle of the Proving Ground; in exchange it would provide maintenance and supervision of the (now rusting) 50-mile fence surrounding the grounds. (47)

In 2000 the Big Oaks National Wildlife Refuge opened. Its website shows beautiful photographs of lakes, woods and meadows. Tim Maloney of the Hoosier Environmental Council was very enthusiastic about the refuge. "It has been allowed to revert back to conditions resembling pre-settlement Indiana," he said. "You have almost a full complement of native wildlife from that era, except for a few large predators." (48) The refuge offered food and shelter for a variety of animal species, including the federally endangered Indiana bat and the state endangered river otter and Henslow sparrow. The place was endorsed by the American Bird Conservancy, as described in an admiring CNN story, "Bombs Give Way to Birds in Indiana." (49) During the flight training exercises of the Indiana Air National Guard, however, the wildlife refuge was always closed to the public. In 2003 seven fighter wings from four states came to Jefferson Proving Ground for test flights, as part of training for the bombing of Iraq. (50) In November, 2004, as the Iraq War intensified, the Air Force announced plans to expand the airspace for military training. Planes would be allowed to fly low over parts of the community outside the limits of the refuge. Only after protests from political leaders, residents (and local pilots) did the Air Force modify its plans. (51)

Even though the UXO and DU were permanently closed off in the wildlife refuge, many residents were still worried. In the late 1990s Richard Hill and other members of Save the Valley began to attend the meetings of the JPG Restoration Advisory Board. (Save the Valley had been established in 1974 to protect the air, water and land between Lawrenceburg and Louisville, and had been active in stopping work on the poorly constructed Marble Hill Nuclear Power Plant in 1975.) The Restoration Advisory Board paid close attention to the Army monitoring of radiation levels at the site. In 2001, however, the army suddenly announced that it wanted to leave the Proving Ground for good. It applied for a termination of its NRC license, arguing that since it was no longer testing depleted uranium, it shouldn't have to stay there. It repeated its claim that the UXO made any kind of cleanup or remediation impossible. The most controversial part of the application, however, was the army proposal to stop all health and environmental testing, on the grounds that it had discovered no uranium in the twice-yearly tests of the ground level water "so far," and that their "computer modeling" showed little risk to the surrounding community. (52) Even the normally military-friendly Nuclear Regulatory Commission didn't like this plan to walk away. After reviewing the (extensive) studies done by Save the Valley, the NRC rejected the army proposal for termination of its license, saying that it didn't have sufficient data to make their "computer-modeling" of community safety credible. (At other military sites where DU was tested, contamination of the ecosystem has been discovered. DU was found in groundwater near a test site in Socorro, New Mexico and in a wildlife refuge near a site in Stillwater, Nevada.) (53) Local residents were also furious about the Army desire to stop the environmental monitoring. Jefferson County Commissioner Julie Berry said: "I don't know why we should be the guinea pigs...A lot can be at stake here. There are a lot of unknowns." (54) A resident named Robert Rosenthal who lived along the area of Big Creek, which flowed right through the middle of the Delta Impact Area, was also alarmed about the Army's decision to stop monitoring. "We have no assurance that stuff won't wash down through here over time....At the very least, there ought to be long-term monitoring downstream of the site. Many of us have wells within a stone's throw of the creek." (55)

In 2003 the Army decided to drop the request for a termination of its license and asked instead to be given a "possession only" license which would be renewable every five years. (56) In February, 2005, however, it returned to the idea of seeking "decommissioning" and total withdrawal, saying that for the next five years it would try to assemble the data the NRC was seeking to prove that the site was safe. The Army proposed collecting data on how much DU was there, the thickness of the contaminated area, and the travel routes contaminants might take to reach the groundwater. It also proposed conducting studies to see if it were possible to determine the rate at which the DU particles were dissolving. (57)

vi

Paul Cloud, the civilian representative for the Army on the Jefferson Proving Ground Restoration Advisory Board, continues to say that army tests of the water at the site are showing no sign of uranium. In meetings in 2003, however, the technical advisor of the Board, Dr. Diane Henshel, an assistant professor at Indiana University's School of Public and Environmental Affairs, said the army should be testing not only the water, but the mussels in the streams, to see if uranium has already entered into the food chain. "The aquatic biota...is where it's going to accumulate over time."(58) According to a report of the Military Toxics Project, an independent investigation by Lockheed Analytical Services has discovered that deer, clams and fish in the Big Oaks Wildlife Refuge may already be contaminated with uranium. (59) At another board meeting concerns were expressed about the toxicity of the depleted uranium in the soil, since even the army has said the toxicity of DU is a genuine health hazard. Participants learned, however, that at the present time no safe toxicity levels for DU have been established *anywhere*. (60)

In 2003 Rep. Jim McDermott of Washington introduced HR 1483, the DU Munitions Study Act, which would require studies on the health and environmental impact of DU testing on places such as Jefferson Proving Ground and Vieques, Puerto Rico (where DU was also heavily tested). Yet Rep. Julia Carson of Indiana, one of the co-sponsors of the bill, said, "We haven't gotten much movement on it," because the government is still refusing to accept responsibility for the effects of DU exposure. Said Carson, "If they accept responsibility then they've got to pay for it, and I don't think they're willing to pay for it." Sick veterans of the wars in Iraq, Kosovo, Afghanistan, and other places where DU has been used, have found this out as well. (61)

At the April, 2005 meeting of the JPG Restoration Advisory Board, the Army said that in late 2004 it had arranged for the removal of 5,800 tons of contaminated soil from the Proving Ground. What exactly was taken, or how this was done isn't clear. Nor is it clear where it was taken; the minutes of the meeting say only to a "certified facility in Kentucky." (62) In June, 2005 the Army came up with a final plan to "extricate itself"--as reporter Peggy Vlerebome put it--from Jefferson. For the next five years, the Army proposed to monitor deer inside and outside the test site for uranium contamination. Members of the U.S. Fish and Wildlife Service would go inside the site, bait the deer, shoot them, and obtain tissue and bone for testing. (63) (An indirect form of deer testing went on at Piketon in the late 1990s, when Bechtel Jacobs "allowed" local bow hunters to come to the wildlife area surrounding the plant and kill deer, with the stipulation that Bechtel be allowed to test the deer for uranium. Bechtel said they didn't find anything, but this was a rather unscientific--and deceptive-- way to monitor radiation levels.) (64) The Army said that the deer tests at the Proving Ground would start October, 2005 and continue for five years, which in conjunction with the well water analyses, would assure area residents that the depleted uranium is not a threat. Though it is hard to see how such tests could be conclusive, given the long half-life of DU, the NRC liked the proposal: "We look at it as a positive step toward decommissioning." (65)

In the summer of 2006, however, new questions were raised about the proposal. Even though Paul Cloud, the army representative, and Richard Hill, of Save the Valley, had agreed in 2005 not to include discussions of depleted uranium in future advisory board meetings (because it was a "health issue," not an "environmental issue") (66), other residents in the community did not want to remain silent. When a study was published in May, 2006 by a Northern Arizona University biochemist about the toxicity of DU causing "mammalian DNA damage," (67) the mayor of Madison, Al Huntington, wrote the NRC, and requested that the Army testing period for Jefferson be extended not five years, but twenty-five years. Unless the Army can "guarantee·sufficient appropriations to fund all aspects of the DU liability," he said, problems will "become the financial burden" of the EPA, NRC and Indiana Department of Environmental Management. (68)   In the fall of 2007 it was announced that the NRC would hold evidentiary hearings in Madison beginning October 22, both to hear testimony about the adequacy of the Field Sampling Plan submitted by the Army, as well as to consider the Army proposal to extend their plans for decommissioning for another five years. It's clear that intense debate about the future of the Proving Ground is still going on. Whether tests continue for another five or twenty-five years, projections will probably not be able to calculate with certainty what the long-term impact of the depleted uranium on species or the environment will be. We only know it will be radioactive for thousands of centuries.

Notes: Jefferson Proving Ground

1. Rad.Alert Conference: "Nuclear Dollars vs. the Common Good." Columbus State Community College, Columbus, Ohio. September 25, 2004.

2. Baker, Sue. *For Defense of Our Country: Echoes of Jefferson Proving Ground* (Greenfield, Indiana: Triad, 1990) , 1-2.

3. Baker 57.

4. Cass, Connie, "50 Years Ago, Their Homes Were Taken for Army Targets," *Lexington Herald-Leader,* May 29, 1991, B3.

5. Baker 32.

6. "Army Investigates Land Deal," *New York Times,* January 28, 1941, 12.

7. Moss, Dale, "Proving Ground Drawing Workers Back," *Louisville Courier-Journal,* August 31, 2005, 1B.

8. McLaren, George, "Site's Wildlife Designation Has Explosive Hitch," *Indianapolis Star,* May 26, 2000, A01.

9. Baker 91.

10. "Bursting Shells Studied at Close Range by Army Men in Bomb-Proof Shelters," *New York Times,* July 5, 1941, 24.

11. Baker 104.

12. Cass.

13. Vlerebome, Peggy, "JPG Opened in 1941...," *Madison Courier,* November 15, 2004.

14. Baker 113.

15. Baker 108.

16. Baker 110.

17. Jefferson Proving Ground Website. (www.jpg.army.mil/main/links.htm)

18. "Man Lives for Weeks in Midst of Shellfire," *New York Times,* October 23, 1955, 32.

19. "Cincinnati Firms' Products Tested at Madison Artillery Range," *Cincinnati Times-Star,* July 7, 1951, 11.

20. "DU Basics." Military Toxics Project. (www.miltoxproj.org/du_basics.htm)

21. Miller, Sunny, "The War Against Ourselves: An Interview with Major Doug Rokke," *Yes! Magazine,* Spring, 2003.

22. JPG Website.

23. Schneider, Grace, "Army's Uranium Worries Hoosiers," *Louisville Courier-Journal,* October 22, 2001, 1A.

24. "Proving Ground is Basic to Defense," *Cincinnati Enquirer,* July 1, 1985, D4.

25. "DU Basics."

26. Malone, James, "U.S.: Weaponry Had Traces of Plutonium," *Louisville Courier-Journal,* January 25, 2001, 1B.

27. "Depleted Uranium." Campaign for Nuclear Disarmament website. (www.cnduk.org/pages/binfo/dpu.html)

28. Bertell, Rosalie, "Gulf War Syndrome, Depleted Uranium and the Dangers of Low-Level Radiation." Canadian Coalition for Nuclear Responsibility. (www.ccnr.org/bertell_book.html)

29. Graham-Rowe, Duncan, "Depleted Uranium Casts Shadow over Peace in Iraq," *New Scientist,* April 15, 2003.

30. Masri, Rania, "Assault on Iraq's Environment," in *Iraq: Its History, People and Politics.* Ed. Shams C. Inati. (New York: Humanity Books, 2003) 189-213.

31. Nixon, Rob, "Our Tools of War, Turned Blindly Against Ourselves." *Chronicles of Higher Education,* February 18, 2005, 7.

32. Schneider 1A.

33. Odendahl, Marilyn, "Will Jefferson Proving Ground Really Close?" *Indiana Business Magazine,* 35 (February, 1991), 33.

34. "Research Needed To Tackle Proving Ground Job," *Superfund Week,* 6 (August 21, 1992), 3.

35. Turque, B. and J. McCormick, "The Military's Toxic Legacy," *Newsweek,* 116 (August 6, 1990), 20.

36. Schneider, Keith, "Toxic Pollution at Military Sites is Posing a Crisis," *New York Times,* June 30, 1991, 1

37. Turque 20.

38. Turque 20.

39. Odendahl 33.

40. Liem, Robert, "Engineering Firm Resets Sights on Site Cleanup," *Lexington Herald-Leader,* February 27, 1992, B5.

41. Wright, Ruth, "The Dean of Deal-Making," *RoundAbout,* April, 1999.

42. "FEMA to Store Mobile Homes Near Louisville," *Lexington Herald-Leader*, September 20, 2006, B5.

43. Thomas, William, *Scorched Earth: The Military's Assault on the Environment* (Philadelphia: New Society Publishers, 1995) 25.

44. "Uranium Buried at Jefferson Proving Ground Worries Residents," *Associ-*

ated Press State and Local Wire, October 23, 2001.

45. Schneider 1A.

46. Weslander, Eric, "Nature Refuge or Bomb Range?" *Louisville Courier-Journal,* August 14, 1999, 1A.

47. Weslander, Eric, "Deal Near on New Wildlife Refuge," *Louisville Courier-Journal,* May 8, 2000, 1A.

48. McLaren A1.

49. "Bombs Give Way to Birds in Indiana," *CNN* March 30, 1998. (www.cnn.com/earth/9803/30/protecting birds)

50. "Southern Indiana Bombing Range Busy with Pilot Training," *Associated Press State and Local Wire,* April 2, 2003.

51. Davis, Alex, "Air Force Has Revised Plan for Fighter Jet Training Zones," *Louisville Courier-Journal,* April 16, 2005, 1B.

52. "Uranium Buried."

53. Bloom, Saul and John M. Miller, James Warner and Philippa Winkler, eds. *Hidden Casualties: Environmental, Health and Political Consequences of the Persian Gulf War* (Berkeley: North Atlantic Books, 1993), 136.

54. "Uranium Buried."

55. Webber, Tammy, "Those Near Base Fear Plan to End Testing of Water," *Indianapolis Star,* November 17, 2002, B1.

56. Vlerebome, Peggy, "Save the Valley Seeks Hearing to Challenge Army's Proposal for JPG," *Madison Courier,* November 29, 2003.

57. Vlerebome, Peggy, "Army Considers Changing JPG Plans," *Madison Courier,* February 16, 2005.

58. Vlerebome, Peggy, "Who Will Clean Up DU Toxic Waste in US?" *Madison Courier,* May 4, 2003.

59. "DU Basics."

60. Vlerebome, "Who Will Clean Up."

61. Healy, Thomas P., "A Deceptively Pretty Place," *Bloomington Alternative,* June 22, 2003. (www.mindfully.org/nucs/2003/du-bigoaks-nwr22jun03.htm)

62. Minutes of Jefferson Proving Ground Restoration Advisory Board. April 27, 2005. (www.jpgbrac.com/documents)

63. Vlerebome, Peggy, "Army Has New Plan for JPG Exit," *Madison Courier,* June 21, 2005.

64. Welsh-Huggins, Andrew, "Bagged Deer Tested for Radiation Near Ohio Plant," *Cleveland Plain Dealer,* October 30, 1999, 11B.

65. Vlerebome, "Army Has."

66. "Last Big JPG Contract Deeded; Cleanup Nears End," *Madison Courier,* April 20, 2006.

67. Braun, Annie, "NAU Team Finds New Danger of Uranium," *Arizona Daily Sun,* May 5, 2006. In addition, a recent study at the University of Southern Maine has shown that DU changes DNA in human lung cells. See James Randerson, "Deadly Dust: Study Suggests Cancer Risk from Depleted Uranium." *The Guardian/UK,* May 8, 2007.

68. "Huntington Wants Depleted Uranium Testing Extended," *Madison Courier,* July 19, 2006.

69. "Atomic Safety and Licensing Board; in the Matter of U.S. Army (Jefferson Proving Ground Site); Notice of Hearing (Application for a License Amendment)." NRC Documents and Publications, October 1, 2007.

Conclusion:

The Hidden Danger

At the present time the six sites discussed in this history are in various stages of remediation. At the end of 2006, Mound and Fernald were both certified as ready for closure, that is, the sites had had the most dangerous radioactive elements removed and what remained--in the soil and water--had been reduced to limits the EPA regarded as acceptable. The remediation of the landfill at Mound has taken longer than anticipated and may not be completed until 2009. Whether the fast-track cleanup has left any residual problems at either Mound or Fernald will only be known in time. The remediation from Piketon's gaseous diffusion operation is still far from complete. Because the gaseous diffusion plant in Paducah is still operating, and presumably will till 2012, its remediation is behind the schedule of the others. The conversion of the barrels of uranium hexafluoride at both Paducah and Piketon does not seem to be very far along, and there may still be technological and economic problems ahead for both. Maxey Flats is already closed. In 100 years, perhaps sooner, the hill of waste there will receive its final plastic, then earthen cap, but will have to be monitored forever, as will the hill of waste at Fernald. If the Army leaves Jefferson Proving Ground some time within the next five years, the depleted uranium there may always remain unmonitored in the ground, though another government agency could possibly initiate inspections in the future. At this time nothing is certain.

The dangerous amounts of tritium, plutonium, technetium, neptunium, americium and other transuranic elements have for the most part been removed from the ground sites in the Tri-state. There is still technetium in the plume at Paducah and traces of transuranic elements in the groundwater at all of the other sites. How much may be in the ecosystem we don't know. The most dangerous sludge and contaminated soil from the Midwest is now out west: at Envirocare (Energy Solutions) in Utah, at the Nevada Test Site, and at the Waste Isolation Pilot Project (WIPP) in New Mexico. Whether the waste will remain contained at these sites for the--in some cases--millions of years it will be radioactive, we have no way to predict. At Maxey Flats, the tritium, plutonium and other transuranic elements could not be completely removed; the blocks of concrete there will have to be under constant surveillance for thousands of years. The Fernald waste from Silos 1 and 2 is temporarily at Waste Control Specialists in Texas; some time in 2008 a decision will be made as to whether it will stay there permanently or be moved again. The plans for high-level waste disposal at Yucca Mountain--where some of the Fernald waste in Texas could go--are still far from complete, and it's possible the site there may never open. A recent news story in Australia said the U.S. government is now trying to negotiate to send its high-level waste there. (1)

If the American Centrifuge enrichment plant becomes operational at Piketon, it will generate new depleted uranium waste, which like the barrels already there, will be dangerous until converted into more stable form. If either Paducah or Piketon is chosen for a nuclear reprocessing plant, spent fuel rods from throughout the country will be transported to the area, and the possibility of accidents or releases from the operations could pose high risks for the Ohio River Valley for a long time to come. If Piketon becomes a storage site for high-level waste, as some of the residents fear, the region could face risks from contamination far greater than those of the past.

ii

This narrative has tried to show the dangerous effects of the nuclear presence in one particular region of the United States. The Midwest was chosen as the site for nuclear installations in the 1950s because it was thought safer from foreign attack than locations on either coast. None of the sites was in a major population center, though Mound and Fernald were both close to large cities. The Midwest had traditionally been regarded as the heartland of the country because of the richness of the land and water. It was the land and water which the military appropriated. Today the Ohio River/ Mississippi River Valley has the highest incidence of cancer of any region in the country. (2) Much of the disease rate may be due to the chemical waste which has gone into the rivers from the industrialization of the region from Pittsburgh southward. Whether the radioactive and chemical waste from the nuclear installations in Ohio and Kentucky has had any part in the cancer incidence we may never know. As said many times, specific nuclear epidemiology is difficult to do because levels and pathways of exposure are hard to determine, the genesis of cancers may take years, and cell damage or genetic effects may not show up for generations.

One of the many unsettling ideas of the Bush administration is a proposed regulation in the Intelligence Reform and Terrorism Prevention Act to limit public access to birth and death records for 70 to 100 years. This regulation would mean that environmentalists or others seeking to do independent epidemiological investigations would be prevented from finding out the general areas where death rates are high --or to check, for instance, what is going on at any of the six sites discussed in this survey. (3) It's possible that crucial government environmental records will also be difficult to obtain in the future. Since 1999 at least 25,515 documents which had been public in the National Archives have been re-designated as "classified" and withdrawn, many from the Environmental Protection Agency. (4) In August, 2006 the EPA announced that agency scientists and outside researchers would be denied access to EPA libraries and collections. Records have been removed from the EPA library website; physical collections of records have been disposed of. All EPA libraries are now under a single political appointee, the Chief Information Officer. (5) The implication of all these monumental changes, so little noted by Congress, is that in the future there may be no way for Americans to find out the full extent of environmental contamination in their communities, including nuclear contamination, or the attendant health risks. As in the 1950s, in the name of national security, the federal government is now appropriating the power to conceal the truth about health and environmental problems from the American people.

The Bush administration has been trying to convince Congress and the American public that nuclear power and nuclear weapons must be brought back. It has never acknowledged the astronomical cost of the perpetual monitoring and management of the contaminated areas we already have with us, which we are leaving as a financial burden and health risk to future generations. Instead it is presenting the argument that nuclear power is a safe, inexpensive way to prevent climate change. This view is disputed by many scientists, who feel that the hundreds of new power plants needed to have any effect at all on global warming would be prohibitively expensive, technologically risky, environmentally harmful, politically dangerous--increasing the levels of weapons-usable material accessible to terrorists throughout the world--and increasing many times over the amount of radioactive waste in the world which we *still* don't know what to do with. The building of new nuclear plants in the United States would cost billions in taxpayer subsidies, and if reprocessing plants were built to generate uranium and plutonium for their operation, the health and environmental risks would be far greater than any we have had in the past. (6) The nuclear industry would have us believe that their nuclear technology has been perfected, that the mistakes of the past would never occur again, that in the future there would be no accidents, no malfunctions, no miscalculations, no leaks, no spills, no faulty products, no cutting corners to save costs, no rushed research, no distracted employees, no EPA violations, no corporate greed, no thefts, no cover-ups, no transportation accidents, no computer glitches, no funding cutbacks, no tornadoes, no earthquakes, no floods, no birth defects, no cancers, no problems with the storage of high-level waste. Sometimes nuclear opponents are called idealists, out of touch with reality, but it's hard for me not to feel that it is the nuclearists who are the ones living in a fantasy world, which they are trying to convince the rest of the world has some validity. The need for global cooperation on the issues of radioactive materials, environmental contamination and nuclear waste has never been greater, but never has there been less government commitment to scientific integrity, international diplomacy and dialogue.

Given that Congress has spent over $7.5 *trillion* taxpayer dollars in the last 60 years on the nuclear weapons program (7), and given that the nuclear industry is so powerful again in the present administration, nuclear opponents like myself sometimes feel like Paducah worker Joe Harding, that we are "fighting a tiger with a toothpick." What has inspired me to write this narrative has been the example of the ordinary people whose lives I have tried to chronicle here-- the workers, neighbors, journalists, scientists, doctors, environmentalists, union leaders, writers, lawyers, whistleblowers, politicians, and community activists-- who have been willing to challenge the lies of the federal authorities and describe nuclearism for the deadly reality it is. It was Americans who began the nuclear catastrophe; it is now up to us to contain the damage we have already caused, and prevent the devastation from going further.

Notes: Conclusion

1. Mark, David, "Australia Could Become US Nuclear Waste Dump," *Australian Broadcasting Company News,* July 20, 2007.

2. "Cancer's Geography in the USA," *Consumer Health Journal,* January, 2004.

3. Allen, Terry J., "Information is Power," *In These Times,* February, 2006, 62.

4. "Keeping the Public in the Dark," *Friends Committee on National Legislation Washington Newsletter,* June, 2006, 7.

5. "EPA Scrubbing Library Website to Make Reports Unavailable," *Common Dreams Progressive Newswire,* December 7, 2006. See also Leslie Burger, "Keep the E. P. A. Libraries Open," *New York Times,* December 8, 2006, and "EPA Resumes Quietly Dismantling Library System: Environmental Prosecutions at Risk from Loss of Original Documents and Cost," *Common Dreams Progressive Newswire,* May 2, 2007.

6. The arguments against the revival of nuclear power are discussed extensively in Brice Smith's *Insurmountable Risks: The Dangers of Using Nuclear Power to Combat Global Climate Change (*Takoma Park: RDR Books/IEER Press, 2006). (www.ieer.org/reports/insurmountable risks) and in Helen Caldicott's *Nuclear Power is Not the Answer* (New York: New Press, 2006.)

7. Cirincione, Joseph, "Lessons Lost," *Bulletin of the Atomic Scientists,* November/December, 2005, 47.

APPENDIX A:

U.S. NUCLEAR FUEL CYCLE

1. Uranium mines
2. Uranium mills
3. Conversion of yellowcake to UF6
4. Low-level enrichment (to 3-5% U-235 for nuclear power plants)
5. High-level enrichment (to 90%-97% U-235 for nuclear weapons and nuclear submarines)
6. Fuel fabrication
     a) fuel rods for nuclear power reactors
     b) components for nuclear warheads
7. Feed production materials
8. Nuclear testing
9. Current inventory
     a) nuclear power plants
     b) nuclear weapons
     c) radioactive waste

1. **Uranium Mines**
   There are three kinds of uranium mines: open pit mines, the excavation of shallow deposits where uranium ore is plentiful; deep mines, which were poorly ventilated in the early years, causing workers to inhale large amounts of radon gas and dust; and in situ leaching, where a liquid solution is forced through underground ore to dissolve the uranium, which is then pumped to the surface in leachate form. The chemicals used in this process are hazardous to the environment. In 2004 there were six mines in the U.S., half of them *in situ,* located primarily in Nebraska, Wyoming and Utah. In the past there were mines in Arizona (on Navajo land), Colorado, New Mexico, Texas, and Washington.

2. **Uranium Mills**
   Mills are usually located near the mines. Their function is to grind the ore to extract the uranium, a process which results in yellowcake. Radon gas, released in the milling process, has been hazardous to workers. The rocks which remain after the extraction are known as mill tailings, which are also hazardous.

3. **Conversion Facilities**
   In the conversion process the impurities of the yellowcake are removed. Uranium is combined with fluorine to make uranium hexafluoride gas ($UF6$). The $UF6$ is then pressurized and cooled to a liquid form and drained into 14-ton cylinders where it solidifies after cooling for about five days. In the past there were three conversion facilities in the United States to convert the yellowcake to $UF6$: at Paducah; at ConverDyne in Metropolis, Illinois (across the river from Paducah); and at Sequoyah Fuels Corporation in Sallisaw, Oklahoma. The Metropolis plant, initially run by the AEC, is now a division of Honeywell International and is the only one still operating.

4. **Low-Level Enrichment (3-5%)**
   The enrichment plants at Oak Ridge and Paducah used the gaseous diffusion method to create low-enriched uranium. $UF6$ gas was pumped through nickel barriers in miles of glass pipes of a cascade in order to separate the fissionable U-235 from the heavier U-238 (depleted uranium). The uranium was enriched from the level of 0.711% U-235 to 3-5%. It was then shipped to Piketon for further enrichment or used as fuel in nuclear power plants. Today the Paducah gaseous diffusion plant is the only enrichment facility still operating; it is due to close some time between 2010 and 2012. The gaseous diffusion method requires vast amounts of coal-generated electricity; coal plant emissions have been responsible for extensive atmospheric pollution. European countries use a centrifuge model of enrichment which requires less electricity, though it still generates waste. A European-style centrifuge is now being built by LES in Eunice, New Mexico. USEC has been developing plans for an American-designed centrifuge for Piketon since 2004.

5. High-Level Enrichment (90-97%)

The gaseous diffusion plant at Piketon received low-enriched uranium from Oak Ridge and Paducah and enriched it further, to 90-97% U-235. This high-enriched uranium was used in nuclear weapons or as fuel for nuclear submarines. Piketon stopped the high-level enrichment in 1991.

6. Fabrication Plants

a) Fuel fabrication plants convert the low-level UF6, after enrichment, into uranium dioxide powder and press it into pellets. These ceramic pellets are loaded into long tubes made of a non-corrosive metal. Joined together these fuel rods form a fuel assembly, which make up the core of a nuclear reactor. The corporations involved in fabrication today are Framatome ANP, Ltd. (Lynchburg, VA and Richland, WA), Global Nuclear Fuel (Wilmington, NC) and Westinghouse Electric (Columbia, SC).

b) High-level enriched UF6 from Piketon was sent to the Y-12 plant in Oak Ridge, Tennessee, which fabricated the highly-enriched uranium components for use in weapons.

7. Feed Materials Production

Yellowcake from the uranium mills was sent to Fernald for conversion through chemicals into uranium trioxide, then heated to produce uranium tetrafluroide (green salt), then finally high purity uranium ingots. These ingots were sent to Ashtabula, Ohio for extrusion, then to Hanford and Savannah River for use in plutonium-production reactors and reprocessing plants, as part of the production of nuclear bombs.

8. Nuclear Testing

From 1945 to 1963 the U.S. government tested nuclear weapons above-ground in Nevada, Alaska, and the South Pacific, causing radioactive fallout to contaminate the air, land, water, and food supply. Human beings worldwide may carry elements created by these tests for tens of thousands of years. The Partial Test Ban Treaty of 1963 was signed by many nuclear and non-nuclear nations (including the U.S.) to stop above-ground testing. The U.S., however, continued to test bombs underground at Nevada until 1992. The Comprehensive Test Ban Treaty of 1996, which most of the countries of the world signed, was not ratified by the United States.

9. Present Nuclear Inventory

a) Nuclear power plants. There are presently 103 nuclear power plants in the United States. All are aging, having been designed to last 40 years. Over a third have received 20-year extensions of their operating license, and over a third more have applied for license renewals. As part of his energy bill, George W. Bush allocated $15 million in industry subsidies for the building of seven new nuclear power plants. Duke Energy (presently provider of power for Cincinnati) is seeking to build the first **new** nuclear power plant in 30 years in **Gaffney**, South Carolina.

b) Nuclear weapon storage. There are still nearly 10,000 nuclear warheads in the U.S. arsenal. About 1,700 warheads are on submarines; about 400 are in bases in Europe (Belgium, Germany, Italy, the Netherlands, Turkey and Great Britain). More than 2/3 of the weapons are stored at ten military bases in the United States.

c) Radioactive waste

1. Low-level radioactive materials. Radioactive waste has been produced at every stage of the nuclear production cycle. The DOE has dozens of low-level nuclear waste disposal sites under its management, including the new one at Fernald. The largest low-level sites are at locations where there has been extensive nuclear production and contamination: Hanford, Savannah River, the Nevada Test Site, Los Alamos, Oak Ridge and the Idaho National Laboratory.

2. Mill tailings. Some mill tailings were left in abandoned sites; some were used in construction projects until federal law stopped the practice in the 1970s. Mill tailings today are stored at sites in the western United States, particularly Wyoming, Colorado, New Mexico and Utah. The radium in the tailings decays to radon gas, which is carcinogenic.

3. Depleted uranium. The depleted uranium U-238 from the enrichment process is presently in barrels at Paducah and Piketon. Eventually it is expected to be converted to uranium oxide residue and hydrofluoric acid, a process which will take about 20 years. It is not known at this time what will happen to the residue, which will be radioactive for billions of years.

4. Transuranic waste. Waste from transuranic elements (those highly radioactive, artificially created elements with higher atomic weights than uranium, including plutonium) is being buried at the Waste Isolation Pilot Project (WIPP) near Carlsbad, New Mexico. When WIPP is full to its legal limit--in approximately 30 years--it will be sealed and closed, but will have to be permanently monitored

5. High-level waste (spent fuel rods from nuclear power plants). Presently the spent fuel rods from nuclear power plants are in cooling ponds near the reactors. It is not known at this time where the waste will be permanently located. Some proposals are that it be contained in reinforced structures near present locations; or that it be reprocessed for use as fuel in nuclear power plants; or that it be buried in underground vaults at Yucca Mountain. The spent fuel rods are the most highly radioactive form of nuclear waste. They will remain extremely hazardous for hundreds of thousands of years.

APPENDIX B:

GLOSSARY

OF TERMS

Atom: The defining unit of an element which cannot be divided or broken up by chemical means. The central nucleus of an atom carries a positive electrical charge; negatively charged electrons revolve around the nucleus.

Atomic Energy Commission (AEC): The first government panel (established in 1947) to promote the development and supervision of the nuclear industry. Criticized for its laxity and conflict of interest, it was broken up in 1974 into the Energy Research and Development Administration (ERDA) and the Nuclear Regulatory Commission (NRC). ERDA later became the Department of Energy (DOE). At least a quarter of the current Department of Energy budget is still devoted to nuclear spending, including that for the military.

Breeder reactor (or fast reactor): A reactor designed to produce more fission-able material than it consumes; sometimes called a **fast reactor** because most breeder reactors use fast neutrons for sustaining the nuclear chain reaction. Other countries have used breeder reactors, but they have not had reliable histo-ries. The only commercial breeder reactor in the United States was the Fermi 1 near Detroit, which closed after a major accident in 1966. Carter canceled the plans for the Clinch River breeder reactor in 1977, fearing it would lead to plutonium theft and weapons proliferation. George W. Bush's **GNEP** is advocating a variant of the fast reactor, which he claims would use reprocessed fuel, take care of waste, and be theft-resistant, but many scientists find these claims dangerous and unproven.

Chain reaction: The continuing process of nuclear fission in which the neutrons released from a fission trigger another nuclear fission, and the process becomes self-sustaining, also known as **criticality**.

Cohort: A group of individuals having a statistical factor in common in a demographic or epidemiological study. The workers at Oak Ridge, Paducah and Piketon have been given **special cohort status** in applying for federal compensation for their illnesses, because of the high-risk conditions of the enrichment environment. Workers at other nuclear facilities are now petitioning to be given the special cohort status as well.

Complex 2030 (Complex Transformation): George W. Bush's plan to modernize the current nuclear complex. It would create a new industrial infrastructure to build the next generation of weapons, possibly up to 125 nuclear weapons a year. The starting cost would be $150 billion, but could eventually be double that. The plan violates the Nuclear Non-Proliferation Treaty and is already controversial.

Conversion: (1) The process of generating uranium yellowcake; the stage before enrichment. (2) The process of chemically treating the barrels of depleted uranium hexafluoride (DUF6)--at the end of the enrichment process-- into uranium oxide and hydrofluoric acid. This second kind of conversion is planned for Paducah and Piketon.

Daughter product: The term used to describe isotopes formed in the radioactive decay of other isotopes. For instance, when uranium decays it passes through twelve radioactive forms (including radium) before reaching a stable chemical form of lead. Radium-226 has ten "daughter products," including carcinogenic radon gas.

Decontamination and decommissioning (D & D): The process of gathering together radioactively charged materials at "retired" contaminated nuclear facilities, and the removal and/or on-site disposal of the waste, so that the sites can pass state and EPA inspections.

Depleted Uranium-238:   In the enrichment process the fissionable Uranium-235 is separated from the heavier Uranium-238 which is not fissionable. This depleted Uranium 238 is still radioactive, but cannot sustain a chain reaction. Great quantities of DU are still stored in barrels at Paducah and Piketon. In solid form DU is extremely hard. It was tested in anti-tank weapons at Jefferson Proving Ground and used in the Gulf War.

Dose reconstruction: An estimation of radiation exposure by considering emissions, environmental measurements and routes of exposure. The process is used in evaluating worker claims that illnesses may have been caused by radiation.   It is not a completely reliable measurement, because of inadequate (sometimes altered records), biological and chemical factors, and (some workers feel) government bias.

Enrichment: The process of artificially increasing the proportion of fissionable U-235 above the 0.711% level of natural uranium, in order to use the U-235 in nuclear reactors and nuclear bombs. Enrichment has traditionally been done by the **gaseous diffusion** or the **centrifuge** method. **Low-level enrichment** (usually 3-5%) provides fuel for nuclear power plants; **high level enrichment** (usually up to 90%) creates materials which can be used in nuclear bombs as well as nuclear submarines.

Envirocare (now **Energy Solutions**):   A private nuclear waste storage facility near Clive, Utah, originally designed only for low-level waste (A, B and C), but now taking in mill tailings as well. Much of the waste from the contaminated sites of the weapons complex (including those sites in the Ohio River Valley) has been taken there. When full--sometime in the mid-21st century--the facility will be closed.

Fission: Splitting the nucleus of an element into fragments. When the fissionable isotope of uranium, Uranium-235, is bombarded by neutrons, its nucleus is divided into two parts; this division initiates a chain reaction which releases massive amounts of energy.

Fusion: A nuclear reaction in which two nuclei are combined to form a heavier one. The fusion of isotopes of hydrogen combine to form a helium atom, which releases a great amount of energy, such as in a hydrogen bomb. (Also known as a **thermonuclear** reaction).

GNEP (Global Nuclear Energy Partnership) George W. Bush's plan to promote the development (and sale) of new nuclear power plants in this country and around the world. Its centerpiece is a plan to introduce new technologies for **reprocessing** spent fuel, which he claims would reduce nuclear waste, but these technologies have not been tested.

Half-life: The time in which it takes a radioactive substance to decay to half of its original activity or strength. Measured half-lives vary from millionths of a second to billions of years.

IAEA (International Atomic Energy Agency): Established by the UN in 1957 to promote the peaceful uses of nuclear energy and to enforce safeguards to prevent the use of nuclear materials for weapons.

Ionizing radiation: Radiation capable of producing electrically charged particles (ions), including alpha and beta rays, non-particulate radiation such as X-rays, and neutrons.

Isotope: One of two or more variant forms of an element. Isotopes are atoms of the same element that have the same number of protons (and hence the same chemical properties) but a different number of neutrons (and therefore different atomic weights).

Linear No-Threshold Theory: A theoretical model proposed by scientists to suggest there is potential biological harm at any level of radiation exposure. The theory is controversial, but it has been re-affirmed by the most recent Biological Effects of Ionizing Radiation report (BEIR VII) of the National Academy of Science.

MOX: A fuel consisting of a combined mixture of Plutonium-239 with natural or depleted uranium. Using plutonium reduces the amount of enriched uranium needed for fuel, but makes the production and use of MOX extremely dangerous for workers and the environment. A MOX fuel fabrication plant is presently being built in South Carolina.

Nuclear Non-Proliferation Treaty: A treaty, opened for signatures in 1968, to limit the spread of nuclear weapons. The five nuclear powers at the time (the United States, Russia, Great Britain, France and China) agreed to start dismantling their arsenals if the other countries of the world would agree not to start nuclear weapons programs. The nuclear powers also agreed not to use nuclear weapons against non-nuclear nations. India and Pakistan, now nuclear, did not sign the treaty, nor did Israel. North Korea signed it but has withdrawn. George W. Bush has in effect nullified the US treaty commitment by funding the building of new weapons, and threatening non-nuclear countries with nuclear attack.

Nucleus: The central core of an atom which composes almost all the weight of the atom. All atomic nuclei (except H-1, simple hydrogen, which has a single proton) contain both protons and neutrons. Protons are positively charged; neutrons carry no charge at all. The nucleus is unaffected by chemical changes.

Plume: A body of contaminated groundwater flowing from a specific source.

Plutonium: A highly toxic metallic radioactive element, very rare in nature, but created artificially in nuclear reactors by bombarding uranium with neutrons. It has 15 isotopes, only five of which are produced in significant quantities: Plutonium-238, 239, 240, 241 and 242. It is highly carcinogenic and considered one of the world's most dangerous substances. Inhalation of 1/1,000 of one gram can cause cancer. **Plutonium-239,** the fissionable isotope used in nuclear weapons and some nuclear reactors, has a half-life of 24,400 years. It was the material used in the Nagasaki bomb.

Polonium-210: A radioactive element, very rare in nature, first artificially produced in the United States by Dayton, later Mound, scientists. It was mixed with beryllium to release neutrons to trigger the chain reaction in the early atomic bombs. It is highly toxic.

Radioactivity: The spontaneous discharge of radiation from atomic nuclei, usually in the form of beta or alpha radiation, together with gamma radiation. All the isotopes of elements with atomic numbers higher than 82 are radioactive, some naturally, many artificially.

Radioisotopic Thermal Generator (RTG): The nuclear-powered battery designed by Mound scientists to convert the heat from **Plutonium-238** to generate electricity for spacecraft during exploration of deep space.

Radon gas. A daughter product of the decay of radium, which is itself a daughter product of the decay of uranium and thorium. It is highly radioactive, and carcinogenic if inhaled.

Reprocessing: The chemical separation of irradiated nuclear fuel into uranium and plutonium--and also fission products, which are high-level waste. Reprocessing is dangerous because of the radioactive fuel elements and the toxic chemicals used. The only commercial reprocessing plant in the United States was at **West Valley, New York**, open for a short time in the 1970s. Billions have been spent on the cleanup at West Valley and are still going on.

Spent nuclear fuel: Fuel that has been removed from a nuclear reactor because it can no longer sustain the production of power. Spent fuel rods are thermally very hot, have to be kept in cooling pools, and are highly radioactive and dangerous as a result of the new radioactive elements created by the fissioning process. At the present time there is no permanent location for them.

Trichloroethylene (TCE) Highly toxic, carcinogenic chemical used extensively in the cleaning of the pipes of the cascades at the gaseous diffusion plants at Oak Ridge, Paducah and Piketon.

Thorium: A naturally occurring, radioactive element, considered by some scientists as a possible replacement for uranium in nuclear reactors. It is carcinogenic, decaying into radium and radon gas. Some research on thorium was done at Mound and Fernald.

Transuranic elements: Artificially made radioactive elements with a heavier atomic weight than uranium (the heaviest element) and an atomic number higher than 92. **Plutonium, technetium, americium and neptunium** are all transuranic elements, very toxic and highly carcinogenic.

Tritium: The radioisotope of hydrogen, the nucleus of which contains one proton and two neutrons. It is almost always found as water, or "tritiated water." It came to replace polonium as the exploding trigger for nuclear bombs.

Uranium: A radioactive element with the atomic number of 92, the last of the naturally occurring elements. Natural uranium is composed of three isotopes: **Uranium-238** (99.284%), **Uranium-235** (0.711%) and **Uranium-234** (0.005%), all of which are radioactive. U-235 is the only isotope which can sustain a chain reaction, and is the one used in reactors and bombs. It is a very hard metal, not dangerous to touch, but if inhaled in gaseous form can be carcinogenic.

United States Enrichment Corporation (USEC): A company created by the Energy Policy Act of 1992 to privatize uranium enrichment for civilian use at Paducah and Piketon. It went public in 1998, but has been plagued by administrative and economic problems. It has invested heavily in the giant **American Centrifuge** at Piketon, but it's not known at this time if the centrifuge will become operational.

Vitrification: The fusing of high level waste into glass-like solids for long-term storage. Even though it is considered one of the safer methods of storage, it is expensive and its durability is still being studied. At the present time vitrification plants exist at Hanford, Savannah River, and West Valley, New York. The vitrification plant at Fernald failed during its test run and was not completed.

Waste Isolation Pilot Project (WIPP): A vast underground storage depot near Carlsbad, New Mexico, which opened in 1999. Supposedly designed only for transuranic waste, it is now also accepting high level waste. Environmentalists are concerned about its long-term durability, given the hundreds of thousands of years the waste will be radioactive.

Yucca Mountain: A Nevada site chosen by politicians to be the location for an underground storage repository for the high-level nuclear waste. Scheduled to open in 2020, it may be postponed to an even later date. It is opposed by many Nevada residents, geologists and scientists.

Sources

Early independent investigations of the problems of radioactive waste in America appeared in the 1980s, in part as a result of the environmental and anti-nuclear movements: Fred Shapiro's *Radwaste: A Reporter's Investigation of a Growing Nuclear Menace* (1981), Harvey Wasserman and Norman Solomon's *Killing Our Own: The Disaster of America's Experience with Atomic Radiation* (1982) and Donald Bartlett and James B. Steele's *Forevermore: Nuclear Waste in America* (1985). The first site-specific study of waste was Michael D'Antonio's *Atomic Harvest: Hanford and the Lethal Toll of America's Nuclear Arsenal* (1993). Two independent studies which appeared in the 1980s, with specific information about the contamination at the Ohio Valley sites, were those done by the Radioactive Waste Campaign of the Sierra Club: Marvin Resnikoff's *Living without Landfills: Confronting the "Low-Level' Radiation Crisis* (1987), and *Deadly Defense: Military Radioactive Landfills. A Citizen's Guide.* (1988).

The major scientific text on the nuclear waste problem worldwide today is *Nuclear Wastelands: A Global Guide to Nuclear Weapons Production and the Health and Environmental Effects* (1999), edited by Arjun Makhijani, Howard

Hu and Katherine Yih. This book presents data from studies which have been done in the U.S., U.K., Russia, France and China. In the late 1990s the Uranium Enrichment Project of the Yggdrasil Institute published independent data about the contamination at Paducah and Piketon. In 2004 Radioactive Waste Management Associates published independent data about the contamination of water sources near nuclear installations, including those in Ohio and Kentucky: *Danger Lurks Below: The Threat to Major Water Supplies from the U.S. DOE Nuclear Weapons Plants.*

The historical information about the six sites in this narrative is based primarily on the work of the extraordinary journalists who collected data and described the problems caused by the contamination. The journalists cited most often are Matthew L. Wald of the *New York Times,* Joby Warrick of the *Washington Post,* James Malone and James R. Carroll of the *Louisville Courier-Journal,* Joe Walker of the *Paducah Sun,* Dan Klepal of the *Cincinnati Enquirer,* Peggy Vlerebome of the *Madison Courier,* and Tom Beyerlein and Lynn Hulsey of the *Dayton Daily News.* I relied heavily on the work of other journalists as well, all of whom cited in the chapters on the individual locations.

Books Cited

Baker, Sue. *For Defense of Our Country: Echoes of the Jefferson Proving Ground.* Greenfield, Indiana, 1987.

Bartlettt, Donald L. and James B. Steele. *Forevermore: Nuclear Waste in America.* New York: Norton, 1985.

Bloom. Saul, John M. Miller, James Warner, and Philippa Winkler, eds. *Hidden Casualties: Environmental, Health and Political Consequences of the Persian Gulf War.* Berkeley: North Atlantic Books, 1993.

Caufield, Catherine. *Multiple Exposures: Chronicles of the Radiation Age.* New York: Harper and Row, 1989.

Coyle. D., L. Finaldi, E. Greenfield, M. Hamilton, E. Hedemann, W. McDonnell, M. Resnikoff, J. Scarlotti and J. Tichenor. *Deadly Defense: Military Radioactive Landsfills. A Citizen's Guide.* New York: Radioactive Waste Campaign, 1988.

D'Antonio, Michael. *Atomic Harvest: Hanford and the Lethal Toll of America's Nuclear Arsenal.* New York: Crown, 1993.

Fernald at Fifty: From Weapons to Wetlands. Ross, Ohio: Fluor Fernald Public Affairs Department, 2001.

Grossman, Karl. *The Wrong Stuff: The Space's Nuclear Threat to Our Planet.* Monroe, Michigan: Common Courage Press, 2005.

Light, Esther. *Miamisburg, the First 150 Years.* Miamisburg: Miamisburg Women's Club, 1968.

McCutcheon, Chuck. *Nuclear Reactions: The Politics of Opening a Radioactive Waste Disposal Site.* Albuquerque: University of New Mexico Press, 2002.

Makhijani, Arjun, Howard Hu and Katherine Yih, eds. *Nuclear Wastelands: A Global Guide to Nuclear Weapons Production and the Health and Environmental Effects.* Cambridge, Mass.: MIT Press, 1999.

Procter and Gamble: The House that Ivory Built. Lincolnville, Ill.: NTC Business Books, 1988.

Resnikoff, Marvin. *Living without Landfills: Confronting the 'Low-Level' Radiation Crisis.* New York: Radioactive Waste Campaign, 1987.

Rhodes, Richard. *The Making of the Atom Bomb.* New York: Simon and Schuster, 1986.

Shapiro, Fred. *Radwaste: A Reporter's Investigation of a Growing Nuclear Menace.* New York: Random House, 1981.

Shrader-Frechette, K. S. *Burying Uncertainty: Risks and the Case Against Geological Disposal of Nuclear Waste.* Berkeley: University of California Press, 1993.

Thomas, William. *Scorched Earth: The Military's Assault on the Environment.* Philadelphia: New Society Publishers, 1995.

Wasserman Harvey and Norman Solomon, with Robert Alvarez and Eleanor Walters. *Killing Our Own: The Disaster of American's Experience with Atomic Radiation.* New York: Delacorte Press, 1982.

INDEX

Agency for Toxic Substances and Disease
   Registry (ATSDR)..................... 19-20, 76

Alvarez, Robert........................... 17. 33, 60-61,
   ....75, 92, 108, 122, 188

American Centrifuge 80-84, 93, 168, 183

Areva 84-85, 94

Atomic Energy Commission (AEC)......3, 9-10,
   ... 16, 43, 45, 95-96, 99, 122, 128-133, 177

Atomic Vapor Laser Isotope (AVLIS) 79

Babcock and Wilcox............................... 21, 84

Base Realignment and Closure
   Act (BRAC).. 155

Bertell, Rosalie 153, 163

Beryllium............................... 8, 18, 53, 78, 181

Bechtel-Jacobs.................................... 50, 55, 82

Big Oaks National Wildlife Refuge............. 158

Biological Effects of Ionizing
   Radiation (BEIR VII) 4, 180

Brown, Sherrod... 28, 87

Bush, George W. 1, 56, 79-80, 86, 116
   ....124, `128, 169-170, 175, 178-181

Casey, Rev. Dahlgren 148

Celebrezze, Anthony 73

Center for Disease Control (CDC) ...19, 76, 104

Chesley, Stanley...............................20, 87, 107

CH2M Hill 26-28

Citizens Advisory Board
   (CAB)......................55, 87, 111, 125, 136

Citizens Against a Radioactive Environment
   (CARE) 105

Clean Air Act 72

Clinton, Bill....................................53, 56, 79

Colley, Vina 75

Colonie, New York 102, 154

Cowdrey, Sharon.....................................19, 29

Crawford, Lisa 106-107, 110-112, 119

Department of Energy
   (DOE).......3, 17, 21, 24-26, 45, 47, 61, 74,
   .... 84, 86, 102, 119, 125, 141, 177

Depleted Uranium 152, 163, 165, 179

DeWine, Mike.....................................18, 76

Dietz, Leonard..154

EG&G 21

Eisenhower, Dwight...................................2, 40

Energy Employee Occupational Illness Compensation Program 53, 87

Energy Solutions (Envirocare) ....82, 84, 114, ...116-117, 123, 128, 141, 168, 179

Environmental Protection Agency (EPA) .... 8, 11, 15-16, 21-22, 37, 31, 50, ...58, 66, 68-69, 73, 82, 107, 113,119, ... 122, 129, 133, 136-140, 143-145, ...161, 167, 169-170, 172, 178

Farollon Island 128, 129

Federal Advisory Committee Act (FACA) 88, 94

Fernald Preserve... 118

Fernald Residents for Environmental Safety and Health (FRESH) 106

Fluor.... 73, 80, 93, 110-113, 116-120, 125, 187

Formerly Utilized Site Remedial Action Program (FUSRAP) 8

Glenn, John 22, 34, 73

Global Nuclear Energy Partnership (GNEP).....................................56, 87, 180

Gofman, John 12

Goodyear Atomic Corporation 65, 73

Great Miami Aquifer............10, 16, 22, 95, 111

Great Miami River ....7, 10, 15, 19, ...95, 101, 105, 108, 110-111

Grossman, Karl 32, 34-35, 187

Groves, Leslie 38

Gulf War 2, 152-154, 163-164, 187

Hanford ....2, 17, 40, 434-44, 47, 77, ... 82-83, 99, 101-103, 107-108, 122, ... 129-130, 175-176, 183, 185, 187

Harding, Joe 48, 170

Hargan, Harold.......................................47-48

Hayes, John P....................................... 133

Hill, Richard.......................................158, 161

Huntington, Al....................................161, 165

Idaho Falls.......................22, 25, 110, 114, 129

Intelligence Reform and Terrorism Prevention Act International Atomic Energy Agency (IAEA) 169

International Nickel Company (INCO) 70

Iraq War 152, 158, 179

Kentucky Ordnance Works (KOW) 38-39

LES 81, 174

Libya 83, 93

Linear No-Threshold Theory...................... 180

Los Alamos 14, 17, 29, 40, 58, 127, 176

Low-Level Radioactive Waste Policy Act (1980) 136

Luken, Tom......................................73, 107

Makhijani, Arjun ....33, 55, 58, 62, 91, 94 ....117, 124, 185, 187

Martin Marietta 49, 54, 73-74

Mason, Bobbie 38, 56, 58-59, 142, 145

Maxey Flats Radiation Protection Association...133

Miamisburg Environmental Safety and Health (MESH)..............................19

Miamisburg Mound Community Improvement Corporation (MMCIC) 24, 29

Monsanto.....................................8, 10, 13, 21

Mound Advanced Technology Center......24, 28

NAC International...86

National Emergency Company (NECO) Later, U. S. Ecology 130-135, 141

National Institute for Occupational Safety and Health (NIOSH).................. 29, 75-76, ...106, 114-115, 124

National Lead of Ohio..........................97, 100, ...102, 107, 109, 116

Neptunium-237 .... 43-44, 49

Nevada Test Site .. 1, 55, 73, 114, 116, 168, 176

Nixon, Richard 72, 163

NIRS 27, 45, 56

NL Industries...102, 116

Nuclear Regulatory Commission (NRC)........... .... 49, 83, 128, 143, 152, 157, 159, 177

Nye, George D. 64

Oak Ridge .... 15, 17, 38-41, 47, 50, 53-54, ...65-66, 70-72, 82-83, 91, 99, ...102, 106, 114, 129, 174-178, 182

Ohio EPA 8, 22, 31, 66, 68-69, 82, 107

Ohio River.............3, 5, 7, 38-40, 49-50, 64-65, ...85, 95, 111, 148, 168-169, 179

On-Site Disposal Facility (OSDF)...............118

PCB 49, 51, 69

Piketon/Portsmouth Residents for Environmental Safety and Security (PRESS) 75

Plutonium-235...14

Plutonium-238...... 12-13, 17-18, 23-24, 27, 181

Plutonium-239....... 12, 43-44, 49, 132, 180-181

Polonium-210 .... 8-9, 12, 17, 181
Powell, Nancy 130-132, 139-140, 143-144
Price-Anderson Act 24
Radioisotopic Thermal Generator
   (RTG) 25, 181
Radium-228 .... 27, 101
Ray, Sam 77, 90, 92
Reagan, Ronald 73, 105, 110
Reprocessing, or reprocessed
   uranium 43-44, 56-57, 62, 101, 182
Resnikoff, Dr. Marvin 32, 90, 120, 132,
   .... 135, 143-144, 185, 187
Richardson, Bill.. 53
Rocky Flats 2, 17, 25, 110, 114, 117
Savannah River 17, 26-27, 3543, 99, 102,
   .... 107, 110, 129-130, 175-176, 186
Save the Valley 157-159, 161, 164
Scioto River....................... 64-65, 68-70, 77, 86
Simmons, Harold.. 116
Skull Valley, Utah 86
Snake River Alliance............................... 25, 34
SNAP-9A 12-13
Southern Ohio Diversification
   Initiative (SODI) 86
Southern Ohio Neighbors Group
   (SONG) 87, 89, 94
Southern Ohio Nuclear Integration
   Cooperative (SONIC)............................. 86
Strickland, Ted 76, 79

Technetium-99 ....43, 45, 50-51, 58, 67
Thomas, Charles...8, 10
Thorium........................... 15, 101, 117, 121, 182
Timbers, William 74, 79-81, 83
Trichloroethylene (TCE).......49-50, 69, 82, 182
Tritium 11, 16, 27, 31, 33, 135, 138, 182
Truman, Harry S................................... 9, 39-40
Union Carbide 38, 41, 44-45, 48-49, 65, 89
United States Army 121, 137, 150, 152-167
United States Enrichment Corporation
   (USEC)...............................54, 73, 89, 183
Uranium Disposition Services............ 54-55, 82
Uranium Enrichment Enterprise............... 72-73
Uranium Hexafluoride......39, 41-42, 54, 66, 69,
   .... 75, 83, 102, 104, 152, 167, 174, 178
URENCO 79, 81
Vitrification...113, 183
Voelz, George 17
Voinovich, George 24, 34, 76, 84, 87
Waste Control Specialists (WCS) 116, 168
Waste Isolation Pilot Project
   (WIPP) 26, 168, 176, 183
Westinghouse 81, 107-110, 135, 175
West Valley, New York 57, 130, 182-183
Wilkinson, Wallace 136
Wooden, Morris 156
Yocum, Edwa.......................................104, 114
Yucca Mountain 86, 128, 141, 168, 176, 183

Acknowledgements

I am indebted to the writing, actions, and commitment of all those in the environmental, anti-war and anti-nuclear movements the last 30 years, particularly Denise Levertov and Marion Bromley, to whom the book is dedicated. I am also indebted to the Intercommunity Justice and Peace Center in Cincinnati, for its support of this project and of non-violent activism in general, and to the librarians at Xavier University and the Public Libraries of Cincinnati and Hamilton County, who gave assistance in acquiring materials. The following individuals read the manuscript and made important critical suggestions: Staughton Lynd, Dr. Michael Adams, Dr. Saad Ghosn, John Irwin, Dr. Herbert Shapiro, Dr. Nancy Spence, Dr. Susan Adams and Mona Weiner. I am indebted to Wendell Berry for his encouragement and support, and to Jim Krailler and Devin Kennedy for their assistance in the book's production.

ABOUT THE AUTHOR

Carol Rainey was born in Cincinnati in 1942, and has lived there most of her life. She is a writer and college teacher.